THE GIRL WITH
THE SILVER CLASP

Juliet Greenwood has always been a bookworm and a storyteller, writing her first novel (a sweeping historical epic) at the age of ten. After graduating in English from Lancaster University and with a postgraduate degree from King's College, London, she worked on a variety of jobs, from running a craft stall at Covent Garden, to teacher, fundraiser and academic editor and proof-reader. She has also run her own award-winning charity, with the aid of Lottery funding and grants from BBC Children in Need, focusing on storytelling workshops with adults and children, including for Women's Aid and the NSPCC.

She has previously published four novels, two of which reached the top five in the UK Kindle store.

Juliet is a passionate lover of gardens and coastal walks, as well as dog walking in all weathers, always with a camera to hand.

Also by Juliet Greenwood

The Ferryman's Daughter

THE GIRL WITH THE SILVER CLASP

Juliet Greenwood

ORION

First published in Great Britain in 2021 by Orion Books,
an imprint of The Orion Publishing Group Ltd
Carmelite House, 50 Victoria Embankment,
London EC4Y 0DZ

An Hachette UK company

1 3 5 7 9 10 8 6 4 2

A CIP catalogue record for this book is
available from the British Library.

ISBN (Mass Market Paperback) 978 1 4091 9660 0
ISBN (eBook) 978 1 4091 9661 7

Typeset at The Spartan Press Ltd,
Lymington, Hants

Printed and bound in Great Britain by Clays Ltd,
Elcograf S.p.A.

www.orionbooks.co.uk

For Victoria Oundjian
With love – and many thanks for the journey!

Prologue

Cornwall, 1909

It gleamed within her hands. Jess turned the delicate oval resting on her palms this way and that to catch the last of the sun.

Around her, the light was dying. Up here, on the fields above the little cove, the line of Cornish cliffs ranged into the distance, vanishing into nothing. Below, the smoke of cooking fires spiralled lazily up from the cottages clustered around the little harbour, intertwining as the night breeze stirred, bringing with it the fishy hint of shells and seaweed. In the stillness and the vastness, it felt as if there could be no one else in all of existence, just her, standing among meadow flowers, watching the world close in on itself.

In the encroaching dusk, the ornament in her hands glowed as if with an inner light, taking her breath away. She drank in the stylised pattern of wild honeysuckle etched into the silver surround, the centre a swallow in flight, blue enamelled wings set against the tart green of springtime. Something inside her shifted, as if her child's body had taken the first twist of the chrysalis, as the butterfly began to emerge into the form it was always meant to find. The kind of emerging from which there is no going back, however hard you try.

'Beautiful,' she breathed into the chilling air. In her short life, she had never seen a rich woman's jewels from a distance, let alone so close she could make out every detail. And this wasn't the setting of diamonds or rubies torn from the earth to flaunt a rich man's wealth. This was different. Something that had set her insides stirring in a way she had never felt before.

'Work of a true craftsman, that,' Mr Wilkes from the harbour's forge had told her, as he laboured on the tricky business of mending the worn and much-loved heirloom, sent down for his attention from Mrs Bellamy of Enys Hall, the mansion overlooking the harbour and all their lives. 'Tricky piece of enamelling, getting them wings such a deep blue. A real beauty.' He had smiled, his face creasing into a myriad of wrinkles. 'But that's not the real skill of it, not by a long shot.' He gestured with his head towards his son, engrossed in mending a broken pocket watch belonging to the local doctor. 'Like I were showing young Ben here, it's the mechanism that's the real genius.'

'Mechanism?' Jess had bent forward as the old man lifted the swallow slightly from its silver base.

'Like them clocks and watches we're always being asked to mend. Only this were meant to be taken apart to make different bits of jewels. Pity to have to be soldering it together, but that's what Mrs Bellamy wants.'

'You're the one mending it, Dad,' Ben said, coming over to join them.

'Aye, but Mrs Bellamy's the one paying. And she's right. It's too thin and worn to mend again and, being her grandmother's, she's afraid of it breaking beyond repair. I don't blame her wanting me to keep it as a hair clasp and lose the rest.' He beckoned Jess to look closer. 'There's a hinge here, see. Or there was before it broke. If you press that little clip there ... that's the one. See, the swallow comes right off. Now, if you turn it over, you can see where you can thread a ribbon through to make it into a pendant. And see them clips? That's where they fitted into a tiara.'

'A tiara? A real one?' She had stared at the sleek form of the bird, feeling herself tiptoeing to the edge of a fairy tale. 'Like a princess?'

'Aye. That's the one. Only, not a place that goes much for princesses is round here, not even in St Ives. Not much call for tiaras, neither. Mrs Bellamy got rid of that bit years ago. So now only this is what's left.' He sighed. 'I never did have the skill to make such a thing. But Ben has.'

'Not to do something like that, Dad.'

'Well, one day you will, lad. When you've had proper training.' Pride beamed from Mr Wilkes' eyes. 'He has the gift, and the way with metals, see. One day he'll make finery for the richest ladies in the land. He won't be going out on the fishing boats, not my Ben. He's worth more than that, and don't let anyone tell you otherwise.'

Up on the cliffs, Jess turned the clasp again to catch the deep rays shooting out in all directions, as the sun vanished behind a line of cloud. She could still feel the sharp stab of hurt that Mr Wilkes had not included her in his ambitions for the future, which had felt even more unfair when he so often depended on the nimbleness of her fingers and the sharpness of her young eyes, and had even admitted she had a brain that could work things out and was quickly learning to spot where a pocket watch needed adjusting.

She might have the aptitude, every bit as much as Ben, but she was a girl and that meant it didn't matter. There were no two ways about it. Mr Wilkes had only allowed her into his workshop in the first place because she was minded by Mrs Wilkes after school, when Dad was late back from his post of harbourmaster. No one would ever take it into their heads to train a girl to make a silver clasp with an enamelled

3

centrepiece fit for a fine lady. Girls didn't do that sort of thing. Girls cooked and cleaned and had babies and made sure their menfolk were fed and happy. Rich or poor, that was the way it was. The way it had always been and always would be. The God-given order of the steady plod of life in the harbour beneath Enys Hall and the world beyond. One that would never change.

Jess looked down again at the silver clasp. She could feel the hands that had beaten out the patterns and formed the shape of the little bird. She peered through the unknown eyes that had watched a swallow in flight and caught its winged motion, observing in minute detail the fluting of honeysuckle with the passion that had found a way to entice its living vigour into unyielding metal.

Touching the glassy smoothness of the enamel was a kind of reaching out to the unknown man – for it was undoubtedly a man – whose eyes had watched and whose hands had captured the beauty of the world. How could you even begin to create an object that was so beautiful? It made her insides ache. One that, without a sapphire or emerald in sight, was so precious it had been passed down with such loving care from mother to daughter.

Darkness was stealing into the shadows. Soon she would be missed and no one, especially not Mr Wilkes, would ever trust her again with a mission to return his work to the housekeeper at Enys Hall. Slowly, regretfully, Jess took a final glance and replaced the silver clasp first inside its velvet bag, then within the protection of its little wooden box, securing it firmly with the catch.

She breathed in deeply. The air lingered in her nostrils with the scent of sun-warmed grass, edged with salt from the sea and the cooking of herring. All around her, trees gleamed with a more vivid green than she had ever noticed before, the streaks of sunset more brilliant in reds and purples. Pink edges of tiny clouds sailed above, boats setting off across the sea to unknown lands, where everything was possible. Every sense in her body tingled, like nettles mixed with sunburn when the day began to cool.

'It's like waking up,' she said to the first stars as they emerged to hang, shimmering, over the sea. Waking up to the deep longing to capture the beauty around her and create an object equally precious. She didn't know how or why. But she knew that was what she was going to do. One day. And no one was going to stop her.

'Why shouldn't it be a girl?' she challenged the stars. 'Who said it couldn't? If Ben can work with silver, then I can too. Just you see.'

Holding the box with its precious contents tight, she ran as fast as she could through the dampening evening grasses, on towards Enys Hall.

Part One

—

1916

Chapter One

The air was chill that November morning, spray shooting up wildly at the entrance to the little cove with the spent force of last night's storm. Within the shelter of the harbour, the fishing boats set up an uneasy rocking, creaking and rattling, grumbling quietly between themselves.

In the blacksmith's forge at one side of the harbour, seventeen-year-old Jessica Morgan settled the weight of Old Gladiator's hoof against her leather apron, putting the horseshoe in place before tapping in the securing nails. The old shire waited patiently, breath snorting gently every now and again against the hair of the farmer's youngest son, the only member of the family who could be spared to deal with a cast shoe.

'There we go,' she said cheerfully, filing down the edges to her satisfaction. 'That should make him more comfortable.' She released the hoof and straightened up, fishing out a slightly frostbitten carrot from her skirt pocket, proffering it to the soft, questioning lips. The carrot vanished, to sounds of much appreciative chewing.

'Dad says to say thank you, Miss Morgan.' Adam, who had only just turned six, eyed her solemnly, small hand diving into his pocket for the required coins.

'It's a pleasure,' smiled Jess, removing her sturdy gloves to ease the transaction. Adam dropped the coins into her palm and stepped back hastily, eyes still round with undisguised awe. Poor lad, he'd probably thought he was having his leg pulled when he'd been told it would be a female blacksmith wielding a hammer and beating metal into shape, sparks flying into the dark of the forge.

The harbour had been accustomed to Mrs Wilkes helping her husband, but she was a foreigner, a stranger, all the way from her native Black Country, near Birmingham, where they did things differently. Besides, it had always been Mr Wilkes who'd taken the orders and the payment, indisputably in charge, just it should be.

Jess patted Old Gladiator, who was snuffling against her pockets in hope of further treats. 'Last one,' she said, holding out a somewhat jaded carrot that, despite the shortages since the war, could be spared.

Although being worked well beyond retirement, Old Gladiator was one of the lucky ones. He'd strained a muscle and was limping heavily when the rest of the horses were requisitioned at the start of the war. Fit only for shooting, Adam's father had declared to the men who had come to collect him, unable to contain his fury at the prospect of being left with no means of getting the harvest in. And how did they suppose you could win a war when the country starved? Not that his arguments had made much difference when it came to the horses that pulled the plough in spring and brought in the harvest in winter. Even the pet pony from Enys Hall, fat and sleek with ribbons in its mane, had not been spared.

Jess didn't like to think what might be happening to the gentle creatures she had known all their lives, if they'd survived this long at all. When the baker's lad had been back home on leave last summer, rumours had flown around the harbour of man and beast dying alongside each other in the mud of the battlefields, bodies no match for the mechanised power of a new kind of warfare, implacable in its horror.

Jess placed the coins in the tin at the back of the forge and followed her customers outside, breathing in the welcome cool sea air as young Adam led his patient charge up the steep roadway towards the cliffs and the path through the meadows to the distant farm.

In the winter light, the harbour gleamed with new-washed brightness, giving it a quietly cheerful air. After an entire day and night with even the fishermen trapped safe inside their cottages as wind and rain lashed the coast, the little row of shops had opened, women with shopping baskets on their arms pausing to exchange stories of loosened tiles and fences being blown down. One enterprising housewife halfway up the cliff was already hanging out armfuls of sheets and underclothes, determined not to miss the routine of washday at any cost.

'It almost looks like it used to, eh?' Ben Wilkes pushed himself out from under the large motor vehicle parked at one side of the forge, dark hair tousled, overalls grubby with oil and dirt.

'I was just thinking you'd hardly believe there was fighting so close.'

'That you wouldn't,' he replied, cleaning his hands with an oil-stained rag and joining her. 'Apart from the lack of men,' he added thoughtfully.

A flicker of fear started inside. 'Only some, Ben. Many are needed here too.'

'So they are. Although there seem to be more women stepping up to fill the gap every day.'

'You don't think we can manage, then?'

'There's no need to sound so fierce. There were women studying with me at the Birmingham School of Jewellery, and working there too. Many were better than the men.' He ruffled her hair affectionately. 'Why else do you think I agreed to train you in metalwork?'

'Good.' The knot of anxiety eased a little. Ben was as much a part of her life as the harbour itself, woven into her bones. Losing Mum so young, and Dad's time taken up with his responsibilities as harbourmaster, the Wilkeses had been her family for as long as she could remember. She had played with Morwenna and watched Ben being trained up by his father in the metal workshop behind the forge.

Even when Ben had left to further his training in Birmingham, they had known he would be back. It had made sense, to bring new skills to supplement the family's income, with the rich taking up motor cars in place of carriages and even some of the more prosperous farmers starting to use machinery instead of scythes and a horse-drawn plough. But if Ben went off to war...

Jess closed her eyes and shut out the vision brought by the rumours and reports in the newspapers. Ben wouldn't join up. The Wilkeses were Quakers. It was one of their oddities. Not that they pushed their beliefs down your throat, but it was there, a deep conviction that meant Ben would never bear arms. Besides, he had come home to help his mother with the family business when old Mr Wilkes had died of a seizure last year, and what would they do without him? But she was horribly aware that now the first rush of volunteers had gone, and conscription had come in, his call-up papers might arrive any day. Morwenna was terrified her brother would become a conscientious objector and be shot as a coward, or for disobeying orders, despite his faith. You heard such stories.

'That's a ship.'

Jess's eyes shot open. Ben had stepped towards the

quayside, eyes focused on the entrance to the little cove. 'It can't be! Dad said none of the boats went out last night, and there's not a trading boat expected for at least a week.'

Ben stuffed the rag into his pocket. 'That's as maybe, but it looks as if it's heading this way.'

Jess followed his gaze. Sure enough, there was a ketch struggling against the waves crashing high against the rocky entrance to the cove. Around them word was spreading. Several of the shopkeepers emerged, joining their customers in curious stares at the unknown vessel. In the harbour, the fishermen inspecting their boats for damage straightened. A shout went up. Jess saw Dad dashing from the harbour-master's little office on the other side of the quay, shrugging on his jacket.

'Not the Hun, is it?' demanded one of the fishermen's wives, appearing from the next street holding her baby tight, her next-youngest clinging to her skirts. 'My Billy says they've been warned not to fish the deep waters because of them underwater U-boats that can blow a boat right out of the water so there's nothing but timbers left.' Her voice rose in unmistakable panic. 'He said they was preparing for an invasion.'

'Not in broad daylight, Mrs Williams,' said Ben gently. 'I doubt the Germans would mount an invasion for all to see. Just a trading boat blown off course in last night's storm and in need of repairs, that's what it will be.'

A murmur went up from the onlookers as the boat swayed, bent to one side at an impossible angle, sail vanishing behind the white of the next roller. At the last moment, she righted herself, inching a little closer to safety. Friend or foe, it was a seafarer in trouble, and the harbourmaster's responsibility to bring the poor souls inside to safety. Jess watched as Dad swung himself down into the small tug, already filled with eager rowers, which immediately set out across the choppy waters to guide the newcomer towards the quay.

'That looks to have been lucky to survive,' remarked a fair-haired young man in a cashmere greatcoat, appearing at the far side of the motor car that Ben was repairing. 'We were watching from Enys Hall. It looked to me as if it was aiming for St Ives, but couldn't make it. The last thing we need is a shipwreck on our hands.'

'Yes, indeed, sir,' said Ben, a little stiffly. Peter Howells was still watching the tug being bounced through the waves as it made its way towards the vessel.

Jess risked a curious glance at his profile, with its Roman nose and clean-set jaw. Unlike the Bellamys of Enys Hall, high on the cliffs, the Howellses were London folk. Rich as blazes, and most of it from their munitions factories, went the whisper round the harbour. How else could they afford their fancy summer villa in St Ives?

Quite a catch for Louisa Bellamy, now Mrs Peter Howells, and a good thing for the harbour, with the promise of new investment to return it to its former glory, when the Bellamys' Leviathan Trading Company had exported Cornish goods all over the Empire. Not that any of them had seen a penny of investment yet, the wedding having taken place just weeks before the outbreak of hostilities. But once this war was over, it would be a new start for them all.

Peter Howells flicked a touch of salt from the collar of his coat with a fastidious air. 'So, manage to fix it, did you, Wilkes? I'm due back in London tomorrow.'

'All done, Captain Howells. You shouldn't have any more problems.'

'Good man.' A look of relief came over Peter Howells' face; his shoulders relaxed a little. 'I wasn't sure how I was to get the thing mended. Fortunate that my wife wanted to visit her family before we left. I'd no idea there was a skilled mechanic in the harbour.'

'I've learnt to turn my hands to most things,' muttered Ben. 'The best thing a man can do, these days, I find.'

'We could do with men like you at the front. Can never get enough engineers. I can put in a word. It'd be better than going as an ordinary soldier.'

'I expect it would, sir.' Jess could hear the stubbornness entering Ben's voice. Ben had never been good at deference and the Howellses lacked the ties of mutual interest woven between the harbour and Enys Hall over generations. Besides, she knew only too well his time in Birmingham before the war had introduced him to a new world of evening lectures at the lending library and working men's – and women's – unions, fighting for better working conditions and the right of all men and women to vote. She had listened eagerly to his every word, feeling the exhilarating air of a new and bigger world breathing into the harbour, where nothing ever changed. But she felt pretty certain a Howells, whose money came from manufacturing, would not feel the same, and any whisper of being a pacifist was likely to get short shrift.

'They've managed to secure the boat,' she said hastily. 'Dad'll bring them in safely now, but they'll as like need help when they get here.'

'Yes, of course.' Ben sent her an apologetic grin. 'If you'll excuse me, sir.'

'I'll come with you, Wilkes. It's the least I can do.' So much for making sure Ben and Captain Howells never needed to speak to each other again. Jess watched anxiously as the two followed the fishermen hurrying to lend assistance. Luckily they appeared caught up in the drama of the moment, their previous conversation abandoned.

Mrs Wilkes appeared at the door of the cottage adjoining the forge. 'Young idiot,' she remarked, watching her son vanishing among the crowd. 'As bad as his dad. Mr Wilkes were a proper firebrand when I met him. Ben's just the same. You'm a wise girl, Jess. No good getting on the wrong side of a Howells, not when one day he might well have a say over who stays and who goes. It's all right fer Ben, he'll be back to Birmingham once this war's over; we're the ones have to live here, and I'm too old to have to up sticks and start again.'

'He couldn't do that, could he?'

'Talk is, the trading business has been so bad since the war, the Bellamys would have had to sell if it hadn't been fer Miss Louisa marrying and the Howellses' money to keep them afloat.' She grunted. 'If they put money in, they'll want a say of how it's run, you mark my words. My niece works in their munitions factory near London; she can tell you a thing or two about the Howellses. Sharp enough to cut themselves, that's them. Useful thing is a private harbour. Must have had their eye on this one since they been spending their summers in St Ives. Least this way we'll still have Mr Oliver to look out fer us. As long as we've got a Bellamy to fight our corner, nothing will change.'

Jess shivered. For all her excitement at hearing of new ideas and new places, the little harbour was her world, everything she knew, where she felt safe. With a war raging so close, the fishermen were wary of going out too far into the sea. Whenever she had nightmares about enemy ships appearing, or the mysterious U-boats that somehow allowed men to breath underwater, she knew she only had to wake up and she would be back in her own little bed. The moment she opened her eyes, she had Dad to protect her and Aunt Sara to scold her for returning home as grubby as a miner, and what on earth had possessed her to become a blacksmith, when there were surely more ladylike ways of contributing to the war effort?

The war had pulled the little community tighter together than ever, with food grown so expensive and the shortages and uncertainty, all overshadowed by the ever-present fear of the telegram boy bringing the worst of news to the families of those on the front line. Despite whispers of invading armies, she hadn't thought of the harbour ever being broken apart, of it no longer being home.

'You'm done enough for now,' said Mrs Wilkes, patting her gently on the arm. 'That were a good job you did with Old Gladiator; we'll make a proper blacksmith of you yet. I'll get on with the mending of them gates. You go and see what's up.'

'But those gates are heavy.'

Mrs Wilkes chuckled. 'I'll manage. I need you to tell me what's going on. Men don't notice half as well, not even my Ben. Go on then, off with you.'

Jess didn't need to be told twice. Even though she'd seen Dad on his way back, she could never quite breathe until he was safely on land. With the swell so high, even in the shelter of the harbour, and with an unknown ship in tow with who knew what damage, anything could happen.

She pushed through the crowd, reaching the ship as it was being secured at the quayside, with Dad already supervising the disembarking of a bedraggled collection of men and women, more than one holding babies in their arms, small children clutching at their hands. They waited silently on the quay, taking little note of their surroundings, huddled in blankets over damp clothing. A child began to sob, gently shushed in an unfamiliar language.

'Oh my lord,' whispered Mrs Elsworthy from the boot-makers, holding her own baby tight against her shoulder.

Jess joined Ben, who was helping an elderly woman with a rough bandage around her head to disembark. She took the woman's free arm, steadying her, feeling the chill of her sodden coat.

'What happened?'

'Sounds as if they were passengers on a ship that foundered in last night's storm.' He nodded towards Peter Howells, who was deep in conversation with the ship's captain a short distance way. 'The crew saved as many as they could. Many more were lost.'

They lifted the woman onto the shore, where she stood, bewildered.

'Poor things.' Jess's heart went out to the silent group.

'The lad here says he speaks a little English, Captain Howells,' called Dad, as a lanky figure, no more than skin and bones, was ushered onto shore, holding a small girl against his chest. Her arms clung tightly around his neck, head buried in the threadbare front of his shirt.

'Good grief,' exclaimed Mrs Carew, the vicar's wife, pushing to the front of the crowd. 'Where on earth have they all come from?'

'Young Frank Dupont here says they started off from France,' replied Captain Howells. 'The crew of their ship were all lost in the shipwreck. Frank and his sister are French, but the rest are refugees from Belgium.'

'I thought as much,' said Mrs Carew, shaking her head wisely. 'Poor wretches. There have been enough of them arriving since the beginning of the war. They can stay in the church hall tonight, until we sort something out.' She began ushering the bedraggled little band towards the small church at one side of the harbour.

Jess wished there was something she could do. She'd heard of refugees from the fighting arriving in their thousands on the southern coast, all homeless and desperate. Ever since the outbreak of war, copies of newspapers had been devoured, or read aloud to those unable to read for themselves, with their reports of the behaviour of the German army to the unfortunate villagers in the lands they had conquered. Most of it exaggerated, or propaganda, Dad had said; war was a vile thing, whoever might be fighting it. All the same, the tales were impossible to ignore.

With the excitement over, the harbour slowly began to return about its business, but with a more subdued air. Peter Howells finished questioning the young lad who spoke English, and nodded, turning to speak to Dad and the captain. Frank still held the little girl close, but Jess could see that even her lightness was too much for his skinny frame. He was shivering violently in his damp clothing, legs trembling with exhaustion, as if he might collapse at any minute.

'Can I take her?' she said anxiously. He shook his head, grip tightening around his burden. Close to, she could see he was older than he looked, more her own age, which made him skinnier than ever. Dark eyes looked out from hollowed eye sockets in the lined and sunburned face that could almost have been that of an old man.

She glanced towards Ben, who nodded.

'Why don't you come with us,' he said. 'That hall's a draughty old place at the best of times. At least the forge is warm.'

'Forge?' Frank rolled the unfamiliar word in his mouth, frowning at them, as if his brain was unable to take in anything new.

'Fire,' explained Jess, miming the striking of a hammer on anvil. If anything, he looked even more puzzled, but the faintest of smiles appeared at her attempt to communicate.

'Please.' His grip tightened even further around the little girl. 'My sister, she stay with me?'

'Yes, of course.' Jess was horrified. 'We wouldn't dream of separating you.'

He nodded, the taught lines of his face easing a little. 'Then please. Yes.'

Jess glanced back towards Dad, but he was still deep in conversation with Peter Howells and the crew from the stricken ship, and she knew better than to interrupt him when he was on harbour business.

She did not dare try to help Frank while he held onto his sister as if to the last thing in the world. Instead, she fell in beside him, with Ben on his other side, waiting to catch him if he should fall, as he walked slowly and painfully towards the forge.

Chapter Two

Mrs Wilkes was waiting for them when they arrived, having clearly been unable to resist watching the drama unfolding on the quay.

'Of course they can stay here,' she said. 'For as long as they need. Why, you'm wet through,' she exclaimed as she ushered them inside. 'Morwenna!'

'Yes, Mum?' Her daughter's head appeared round a small door at the far end of the forge.

'We need blankets, and there's them old trousers of Ben's we was going to cut up for rags, and any jumpers you can find. And there's them clothes we kept in case.'

'Yes, Mum.' Morwenna stared at the new arrivals before disappearing on her mission.

Frank moved closer to the forge, still holding the little girl tight. In the light of the dying flames, Jess could see steam beginning to rise from their clothes, vanishing into the rows of hammers stacked up against the whitewashed walls, along with chains and rows of horses' shoes, between broken railings, part of an old cart, and half a dozen buckets waiting to be mended.

Morwenna reappeared within minutes, carrying a basket containing a jumble of blankets and clothes. Mrs Wilkes riffled through, pulling out a smallish dress and a coat.

'Don't hold with sentimentality, but it does have its purposes,' she remarked. 'This were Morwenna's favourite when she was small. I were keeping it for when she had a daughter. Well, a good thing, now it's needed. Too big, but it'll do. And this will do fer you, young man.' She held it out towards him. 'For you.'

Frank nodded. Humiliation passed over his face, immediately hidden. The hand that took the garments had an attempt at cleanliness, but Jess could see the ingrained dirt showed the battle had been lost long ago.

'Charlotte...' He put down the little girl, who wriggled and protested in murmurs, hiding her face against him. He undid the broken remains of buttons to release his sister's dress, gently easing off the filthy underskirt, while persuading her to release her arms long enough for him to pull on the dress. It was far too long, but Morwenna vanished again, this time to return with a piece of ribbon she tied around the waist.

'There you go,' said Mrs Wilkes triumphantly, buttoning up the cardigan, which nearly reached to the little girl's knees but fitted close enough to help keep the dress in place. She scratched her head at the shoes, which had been beautifully made but were too small for her and worn to nothing. 'No boots, I'm afraid, but we can find you some socks, dearie. I can't sew to save my life, but I can knit and socks are my speciality. Now, you come with me and let that brother of yours get dry too.'

The girl shrank from the proffered hand, holding on tight to the only anchor in her life.

'What's your sister's name again, dearie?'

'Charlotte,' he replied. 'She not speak.'

'Of course not, poor little thing. No one would expect her to understand English.'

He shook his head. 'Not speak. Nothing. Not since we left.'

'Oh my lord,' said Mrs Wilkes. 'Well, you explain it to her in your own language, and tell her I've some hot soup for her while she waits.'

He bent close, whispering to the little girl as he adjusted her dry clothes, with a hand as practised as a mother's.

Mrs Wilkes caught her lower lip between her teeth. 'Poor things,' she said, with an unfamiliar crack in her voice.

The girl began to look frightened. She shook her head, face disappearing into his shoulder once more.

'I am warm enough,' he said, with an apologetic smile.

'Nonsense, young man, you'll catch your death,' said Mrs Wilkes. 'There has to be some way of distracting her, just long enough for you to change.'

'I know,' said Morwenna. 'You can watch Ben work.'

'Of course.' Jess smiled encouragingly at Charlotte. 'It's magic. Real, proper magic.'

Frank whispered in his sister's ear. She looked up warily, but with a sign of being just a little intrigued. More whispering, and she nodded.

'Good.' Morwenna grinned at Jess. 'You as well. Jess makes the magic, too, just you see.'

Jess found Frank eyeing her curiously as he translated for his sister. Like her brother, she was painfully thin and several years older than she had first seemed. Blue eyes searched Jess's face, as if not quite daring to trust any sign of friendliness.

Jess smiled at her. 'Come on, I'll show you.'

She led the way through the back door of the forge to the small workshop set in the back yard at a safe distance away from the privy.

Even before the war, Jess had jumped at the chance of helping Mrs Wilkes, when her husband had grown too frail to carry on the heavy work in the forge. Female blacksmiths were rare, but not entirely unheard of. Dad had been slightly bemused at this eccentricity, but clearly viewed it as loyalty to Mrs Wilkes and something she'd soon grow out of, especially once she started courting. Aunt Sara, who had come to live with them after Mum died when Jess was very little, muttered constantly about Jess ruining her hands and her complexion, and what man would settle for a girl with a right arm stronger than his own?

Not the sort of man she'd look at twice, Jess had decided, although she tactfully didn't voice this aloud. If Aunt Sara suspected she had a passion that consumed her, or that her dreams were not of princes but the delicate patterns Mr Wilkes and his son formed from metal, Jess knew she'd be dragged back to serving in Mr Hansard the baker's as a suitable occupation. Not to mention it being a prime location for meeting eligible young men, who would be more than ready to fall in love with a girl with flour on her hands, handing out the tastiest of pies as if she had made them personally.

Jess loved every minute of learning to heat metal to the correct temperature to be beaten into shape. She'd learnt to mend gates and fences and even the odd kettle, grown thin from too much service over the fire. Helping with the shoeing of the few remaining horses and ponies had daunted her at first, but, under Mrs Wilkes' tuition, she had gradually gained in confidence. Since the war, she had even begun to learn the inner workings of the motor vehicles that seemed to break down at the most inconvenient moment, with no one quite sure how to confront the mysteries of their engines.

She enjoyed the challenge and the sensation of pushing her body to the limits of its strength, and her mind to the limits of its ingenuity; but it was in the little workshop at the back of the forge where alchemy took place. She still missed old Mr Wilkes, who had been persuaded to continue to allow her to help him most evenings with the mending of broken necklaces and brooches, along with the intricate workings of clocks and pocket watches. But it had only been with Ben's return that she had managed to get some proper training in the working of pewter, working her way towards the finer skills of silver and copper.

It was dark inside the workshop, lit only from the light of a small fire and light streaming in from a deep-set window onto a long workbench.

'Come and have a look, Charlotte,' said Jess, drawing up a chair for the little girl to stand on. She pointed to a brooch formed into the stylised shape of irises in the Art Nouveau style, gleaming in gradating hues of purple against a background of soft green. 'They look like precious gemstones. You'd never guess it was just coloured glass, ground up fine and heated until it becomes liquid.'

'That's the skill in it,' said Ben, looking up briefly up from his work to smile at the little girl. 'Gemstones are just there to be positioned. Enamelling is an art in itself.'

'It's beautiful,' sighed Jess wistfully, watching closely as he returned to forming the patterns. She still despaired of ever being able to match his dexterity in etching patterns into metal before filling them with the luminosity of enamelling. Even before he had returned from the Birmingham School of Jewellery to help his mother, Ben had already attracted commissions from several wealthy families.

Despite the shortages, it seemed there were still those who could afford fine necklaces and earrings. Aunt Sara, who had spent half her life in London, said that her friends were still going out to dances and restaurants and that life must go on. At least it had allowed Ben to gradually build up his little business, training a slightly dubious Morwenna – whose heart was set on creating delicate embroidery that few in the harbour could afford – to help him as his work increased.

One day, he declared, they wouldn't have to mend motor cars to help pay the rent, and Mrs Wilkes could finally retire from the heavy work that you could see was getting too much for her even though she'd never admit it.

Jess secretly hoped Ben would soon be able to employ her to help him as well as Morwenna. She was determined to work hard and learn all she could, until she could create the kind of patterns Ben formed beneath his lithe fingers, jewels that came to life, obeying his every whim.

Next to her, Charlotte was distracted by the sketches scattered over the desk. The fingers of her free hand closed over a pencil.

'Here, there's paper,' said Morwenna, retrieving a scrap of wallpaper Ben had been using for his designs, turning it over to reveal the plain backing. Charlotte hesitated, longing on her face. Still not quite releasing her brother's hand, she made one hesitant line on the plain back of the paper, followed by another, her face gradually relaxing into absorption as patterns began to appear beneath her fingers. The paper slipped a little on the bench, marring the curve imitating the elegance of Ben's flowers. Absently, she freed herself to steady the paper with her left hand.

After a moment's hesitation, Frank vanished discreetly to change out of his sodden clothes, returning within minutes, buttoning up a shirt and shrugging on a jacket that enveloped him, making him appear more emaciated than ever.

Ben soon abandoned his own work, his gaze falling on Charlotte, who was still oblivious to her surroundings.

'I wish my students at the Birmingham School of Jewellery had been so dedicated. And so skilled. That's a remarkable gift for one so young.'

'*Maman* painted . . .' Frank sought a word. 'Very small.'

'Miniatures?'

26

'Yes. Miniatures.'

'Was she with you on that ship, dear?' asked Mrs Wilkes, gently. 'And your father, too?'

Frank shook his head. 'After the soldiers came...' There was silence, broken only by the steady scratch of Charlotte's pencil.

'Well, you're safe now,' said Mrs Wilkes. 'You'll be safe here, you and your sister. Come on, let's find you something to eat and a bed to sleep in until something more permanent can be sorted out.'

'*Merci*. You are kind.' His eyes followed Jess, who was picking up the bowl she was working on, tapping away with a small hammer, feeling as the pewter bent into shape. 'You make?'

'I'm trying to. I'm learning the techniques. I want Ben to teach me how to do enamelling.' At Frank's blank look, she picked up a small brooch to show him. 'With glass. You melt it, then it sets hard and shiny when you polish it.' He nodded. 'Only Ben won't let me until I learn to do this properly first.'

'Trust you to want to run before you can walk,' said Ben, laughing.

'Nothing wrong with ambition,' she retorted. Frank's eyes moved from one to the other, as if trying to work something out. 'It's all right. Ben always thinks he can boss me around, just because he's older than me and I don't have a brother of my own.'

'I don't boss anybody. And anyhow it's pointless, as you never take any notice.'

A faint smile appeared on Frank's salt-chapped lips, his face touched with unbearable sadness. She wondered how long it had been since he had found himself among the easy banter of a safe family home, and her heart broke.

'Do you paint too?' she asked.

27

He shook his head. 'No. I make ...' He struggled to find the words, eyes travelling over the workbench until it rested on a small wooden box Ben used for keeping bits of glass to grind down into powder. 'Like this.'

'You're a carpenter?' His brows knotted. 'With wood?'

He nodded. 'With wood. Yes.'

'Then you'll always be able to make a living,' said Ben. 'There's always a call for carpenters. Before the war, the artists in St Ives were always wanting their pictures framed and shelves built to hold their supplies. With that kind of skill, you'll soon be able to make a home for you and your sister.'

'I hope,' he replied quietly. Across Charlotte's head bent over her drawing, Jess met his eyes. They were dark and haunted. The look of one who would never feel safe again.

Chapter Three

In the elegant drawing room of Enys Hall, on the cliffs overlooking the little harbour, Mrs Bellamy listened intently to her son-in-law's account of the unexpected arrivals.

'And were many lost?'

'I'm afraid so.' Peter Howells glanced apologetically towards his wife. Louisa shuddered and turned away, the rubies of her earrings glowing blood-red in the lamplight.

'Then we must do what we can for the poor souls who have survived such a terrible ordeal. The church hall is no place for women and children. We have enough room to house them here until a more permanent solution can be found. Rachel, my dear, you can help me get the rooms in the west wing ready.'

Rachel Bellamy closed the forgotten book lying on her knee, placing it on the table next to her. 'Can't you ask Cook to release Hannah from scouring pans for while, Mama? I can take the Ford down to the harbour. We can't expect them to walk up so steep a hill. I'll be better employed using my Red Cross training to assess any who are in need of a doctor than making up beds.'

'My dear, Hannah has so much to do already, and we can hardly ask Louisa to accompany you, when she has so little time with her husband as it is.'

'I'm perfectly capable of going on my own, Mama, and

I don't think anyone is going to be concentrating on the proprieties when there are lives at stake.'

'You are quite right,' said Peter, jumping to his feet. 'Those families looked perfectly wretched. I'll help you. Two motor cars will be better than one.'

'But your mother is expecting us to be back for dinner,' said Louisa. 'They've seen little enough of you as it is while you've been on leave.' Her voice grew plaintive. 'Especially with business keeping you in London for so much of the time.'

'It'll only take a few minutes to fetch the babies and their mothers in the motor car,' replied Peter, two points of colour appearing on his cheeks. 'It's the least we can do. We can get back to St Ives in plenty of time to join the others for dinner.'

'Yes, my dear,' murmured his wife, turning her face away towards the fire.

'Good,' said Rachel, making her escape before her mother could launch any further protest. She hastily changed her shoes for more practical boots in the hallway, heading for her brother's Ford before Mama could change her mind. It still held the faint scent of Oliver's cigarettes. One of his coats was flung with his customary carelessness on the passenger seat. The evening was colder than she had expected. She pulled the coat on over her cardigan, feeling the comfort of his presence enveloping her.

She missed her younger brother more than she could say. For as long as she could remember, it had been her and Oliver sneaking off together on adventures, racing down the steep steps cut into the side of the cliff down to the little beach at one side of the cove. Taking out the rowing boat as far as they dared, hugging the rocky shoreline until they reached St Ives. Oliver had volunteered the day war had broken out and was now somewhere in France, with only his letters to reassure them he was still alive.

In those first months she had hoped, like everyone else, that the newspapers were right and it would soon be over. But she only had to see Papa's grim expression and the brittleness of Mama's temper to know that her hope was in vain. Her parents couldn't stop Oliver from volunteering to fight for his country, any more than the Howellses had been able to prevent Peter, who had also joined up in those first heady days of the war, when so many of the young men, rich and poor, had left in a rush of idealism.

Rachel shivered. Neither of her parents had ever recovered from the death of their firstborn son, just three years ago. Reckless Simon, who'd always seen himself as invincible, had been caught in a snowstorm while on a walking holiday in the Alps. Only their guide and one other of the mountaineering group had survived; the rest had been lost to the relentless cold. Such a senseless waste of life, their mother had said, when his body was finally returned. Such a stupid, senseless waste.

Rachel turned the wheel, following Peter down towards the harbour. Life was so fragile – that was the lesson Simon's death had taught her from an early age. So impossibly fragile. To be lost in the turning of a sunny day to ice, or calm waters stirred up by a sudden storm. Now there was war raging across the Channel, with thousands dying every day, yet she was expected to stay at home, unable to do anything useful.

'Are you certain about this?' said Peter, coming to open her door as she pulled up.

She jumped out without taking the support of the proffered hand. 'I can hardly back out now.'

'They were in a pitiful state when I saw them on the quayside.'

'All the more reason to put my feelings onto one side,' she returned, sweeping past him into the hall. The moment she entered, her bravado slipped. For most of her life she had been pressed into her mother's work with the poor, raising funds and taking food and clothing to women who had lost their breadwinner to illness or the sea, but not even the worst of the Downlong area of St Ives had quite prepared her for the wretched tide of humanity crammed into the tiny hall, far too many for the chairs, with most crouched in small groups on the floor. It was the silence that unnerved her the most. No crying babies, no scolding mothers. Just the chilled stillness of the deeply shocked, with no emotion left.

'Poor things, they must have had little enough to start with as it was,' said Mrs Carew, pausing in the making of tea to join her. 'Now so many have lost friends and relatives to the sea. We are attempting to make a list, but it's almost impossible. The women who have lost their children are the most pitiable. I never thought to see so much despair in one place.'

'At least we can offer them warmth and food and somewhere to sleep tonight,' said Rachel, forcing herself to remain practical.

'That's true, and very good of Mrs Bellamy to make such a generous offer. It wouldn't be seemly to house them here with the men. Some of the harbour families have offered, but they have little enough themselves and most have no space to spare. You must convey my gratitude to your mother – this is by far the best solution.'

For the next hour or so, Rachel ferried her traumatised passengers, each to be taken away by her mother the moment they reached Enys Hall. As she returned for her final journey, she stopped to knock on the door of the forge.

'Good evening, Mrs Wilkes. I was told there were two of

the refugees here. We're taking as many of the women and children as we can up to Enys Hall. There's room for a few more.'

'They'll be all right here, miss,' said Mrs Wilkes. 'They'm nicely settled, seems a pity to move them.'

'But you've not much room as it is.'

'My sister's making them up a bed,' said Ben, emerging from an inner room to lead against the doorpost, arms folded. 'I'll be comfortable sleeping in the workshop, Miss Bellamy. They'll be quite safe here.'

'I didn't think they wouldn't,' she returned, bristling slightly at his tone. Even her father's tenants, she recognised with irritation, saw her as a feeble do-gooder, a silly middle-class woman stepping briefly out of an obsession with ribbons to earn her place in heaven before returning to the safe world of romance novels and securing a husband to keep her in unthinking comfort for the rest of her life.

'Ben's right, Miss Bellamy,' said Mrs Wilkes. 'They're safe as houses here. Best give some others a chance of a warm bed.'

'Yes, of course.' She was ashamed of her momentary irritation. This tragedy was larger than her feelings and her dissatisfaction with her own life; she should simply be doing all she could to help. 'Thank you. And if there's anything you need, Mama will be happy to provide it.'

'Miss Bellamy?' As she made her way out into the evening light, she found Ben behind her.

'Yes, Mr Wilkes?'

'I was going to bring this up tomorrow, but if you'd like to take it now it's all ready.' He opened his hand, revealing a small, oval-shaped locket, intricately decorated with swirling patterns of light blue, set around a cluster of darker forget-me-nots.

'It looks like new,' she exclaimed. 'That's just how I remember it. My grandmother knew how much I loved her locket; that's why she left it to me. Thank you, Mr Wilkes. Mama said you were the right person to mend it. So now I can wear it.'

'It was a pleasure, Miss Bellamy.' His voice softened. 'This looks as if it might be Russian in origin. My own skills at *cloisonné* can't match those of a real master. At least not yet. To be honest, I learnt so much from working on this. I might even try the pattern myself, if you don't mind.'

'No, of course not.'

'The mechanism was the tricky part. I'm afraid it was beyond mending, but I made a new catch to keep it securely shut.' He demonstrated, opening up the tiny spaces for portraits inside.

'That's perfect. Thank you.'

'All ready for a new life,' he said, a little wistfully. He closed it again, holding it in his hand as if unwilling to let it go. He had forgotten her, absorbed in the delicate beauty of the swirls of inlaid metalwork.

That was true passion. Not the overblown gestures of the romantic hero in the novel she had so willingly cast aside earlier that evening, impatient with the wilting timidity of the heroine who seemed unable to step a foot outside her door without needing to be rescued. Clear, deep passion. It took her breath away.

'I'd rather be able to make something like that than own it,' she said, without thinking.

He looked up. 'There are many ways of finding a purpose in life.'

'So I've heard.' She winced. Was she really that transparent?

'The trick is to find them.'

34

'Yes.' She held his gaze for just a little too long, the social distance between them forgotten as he tried to make her out, as if seeing her properly for the first time and finding the woman beneath the fine lady from the family who owned every part of the harbour and could have him thrown out on the slightest whim.

Heat went through her, sending shivers shooting through each limb and an unfamiliar tugging deep in her belly.

'Enjoy your locket.' He sounded faintly embarrassed as he placed it in her hand, still soft from his warmth. 'Goodnight, Miss Bellamy.'

Her legs were shaking as she reached the Ford, fingers clumsy as she placed the chain round her neck for safety. The locket rested in the hollow between her collarbones, a gentle pressure she would never be able to ignore.

But there was no time to think. Her final group of passengers were already waiting for her outside the church and the day was fading fast. With all lights forbidden for the fear of Zeppelin raids, she'd no wish to negotiate even the short drive home in the dark.

To her relief, she managed to reach Enys Hall before the day vanished completely. As the small group of women and children were led inside by Hannah – who, as the Bellamy's general maid, had been on her feet since well before dawn and was beginning to stumble with exhaustion – Rachel found Peter propped against the bonnet of his motor car, smoking in the last of the light.

'A good day's work,' he remarked as she joined him. 'I ought to be getting Louisa back to St Ives.'

'Mama said she telephoned your father to let them know you'd be delayed.'

'That was thoughtful of her. But it's late. We will expected back in time for dinner and I don't want to create a fuss.'

He finished his cigarette. 'I've been thinking I might suggest Louisa spend more time with you here after I rejoin my regiment. Papa is determined to take the family back to London for the duration, despite the danger of Zeppelin raids. He's quite convinced that even the Hun won't dare firebomb Mayfair. He may be right, of course, but I'm worried Louisa has no friends of her own there. I don't like the thought of her being unhappy, especially with things being so uncertain.'

'Louisa will always have a home here.' She was tired and still disturbed by the unexpected sensation stirred up by Ben Wilkes just now, and all she wanted was to get inside and be alone with her thoughts.

'Thank you.' Peter extricated another cigarette from his ornate silver case, inlaid with mother-of-pearl. As he held the match to the end, she could see his hand was shaking. The sudden flare revealed his face, less formal than his usual expression. Younger, more mobile. More vulnerable.

Rachel hesitated. Under normal circumstances, she barely exchanged more than a few words with her brother-in-law, thankful that he avoided all but the most superficial conversation. She might not be a beauty, or known for her sparkling wit, but his pride was clearly still offended by her pointed refusal to respond when he first began his visits to Enys Hall, signalling her, as the eldest daughter, out for his attentions.

Papa had been delighted at seeing the prospects for his most troublesome child; the one who, despite much schooling in the art of being pleasant and demure, had never quite been able to resist expressing her own opinions, so acquiring the reputation of a bluestocking and not the kind of wife to be relied upon to spend her days soothing her husband's brow. Papa had been openly relieved he might not find himself with a daughter left on the shelf after all, and deeply disappointed that it had been Louisa, who had a dozen suitors flocking around her already, who had eventually become Mrs Peter Howells.

'Louisa said you are rejoining your regiment at the end of the week.'

'Yes. I have to go to London first – I'll be joining them from there.' He was silent for a minute. 'Rachel, can I ask you to do something for me?'

'If you wish.'

'Take care of Louisa? I mean, if I don't make it, that is.'

A jolt went through her. The possibility of Peter not returning was something they never discussed. For all they knew otherwise, it was still something that happened to other families, not them. It was unthinkable. 'Yes, of course I would.'

'She is so very trusting. I've asked Tobias to take care of the practicalities and make sure she is looked after, of course.'

'Oh,' said Rachel, biting back the urge to say that the last person she'd ever want looking out for those she loved was Peter's younger brother. There was something about Tobias that set her teeth on edge. It wasn't so much that he treated her with undisguised contempt, but that he appeared so confident of his own future glittering success, even after word spilled out that he had failed his Oxford examinations miserably. He seemed to assume a place would be bought for him by his father as his right, as if such things as examinations only applied for lesser mortals. Tobias didn't strike her as someone who would look out for anyone's interests other than his own.

'But I still feel she needs her own family too. I'm not sure how she might cope if left on her own.'

'Louisa is stronger than she looks.'

'I expect so.' He wasn't really listening. She could make out

37

his shadow in the encroaching dark, lost in his own thoughts, cigarette forgotten in his hand.

'And it won't come to that.'

He roused himself a little. 'Yes, I'm sure you are right.' He reached for his matches, this time turning away from her, cupping his hands to protect the flame from the breeze coming in from the sea. 'I've grown very fond of her, you know.'

Rachel blinked. This sounded like the start of an embarrassingly personal conversation, one that she was not sure she should be having with a man. One that, with her own confusing emotions still swirling inside, and the locket pressing like a stone against her bare flesh, she was quite sure she didn't want to hear.

'Mama will be expecting me.'

'The thing is ...' His voice struggled. 'The thing is, I have to make it right. Seeing those men and women who have lost everything, just now, made me realise she is right. I've been a fool. A blind, selfish fool. I have to do something, before it's too late.'

'I see.' She couldn't quite keep the sharpness at bay. His head shot up, eyes glinting in the reflected light from the evening sky. Temper stirred, sharpened by the desperation she had just seen and heard among the wretched survivors of the shipwreck.

Did he really think she had avoided his advances out of squeamishness? Or that her lack of warmth towards him as Louisa's husband had been some kind of female jealousy of domestic bliss, rather than an overwhelming urge to box his ears?

She still wanted to shake him for thinking he could just live his life unquestioned, as if Louisa being whispered about and pitied didn't matter. More to the point, Louisa sensed it.

'Did I ever tell you that when I stayed with Aunt Flora in London, not long after you first came to visit us at Enys Hall, she took me to the theatre?'

'Perhaps we should join the others,' said Peter.

He wasn't getting away with it that easily. 'There was a young actress she particularly wanted to see,' she went on. 'I thought it was odd she should take such an interest when it wasn't the leading lady, not even a particularly important part. But then Aunt Flora never can resist gossip, especially when it has more than a hint of scandal. She assumed I was too sheltered to understand.'

Peter pushed himself off from the bonnet, stubbing out the end of his cigarette beneath his boot. 'I think we'd better go inside. Louisa will be getting anxious.'

'I don't know much about acting, but she was very beautiful.'

'Not just beautiful,' he snapped, as if unable to help himself.

'So I could see. My aunt was disappointed. I couldn't say what she expected, but it was clear that the young woman was working hard at her craft, the kind of dedication that might mean she could one day be the leading lady. Even I could understand that whenever she was on stage, your eyes just gravitated towards her. She was mesmerising.'

There was a moment's silence. She couldn't help taking a touch of satisfaction in his discomfiture. She and Louisa might have very little in common, but Louisa was her sister and no one humiliated her in that way and got away with it.

She took enough pity on him to bite her lip about the following day, when Aunt Flora had taken her to the glittering splendour of Barringtons, one of the new emporiums on Oxford Street. Her aunt had made the most of being a highly valued customer. It seemed she had, temporarily forgotten that she'd given up trying to fit her eldest niece into the mould of a lady and debutante, the day she turned eighteen and her rebellious streak could no longer be contained. None of the gowns she had selected for Rachel were quite right. She had insisted on the department summoning its mannequin, one of several young women employed to display the choices of its well-heeled lady customers. When Rachel saw her, she had had to suppress a gasp.

Miss Giselle Harding had been made to put the gowns on, one after the other, again and again, parading up and down for hours on end. Aunt Flora had made sure the part-time actress knew exactly who they were, her eyes watching every move, inspecting every last curve of her figure with a critical eye that had had nothing to do with the cut of each gown, ostentatiously taking notes to pass to ladies over afternoon tea and any others of her social circle who would listen.

Peter was fiddling with his cigarette box. 'Will you tell Louisa?'

'No, of course not. She's my sister. I'd do anything to prevent her from being hurt. But you are right. She would be better here with us for the duration of the war, rather than staying in London.'

'Thank you.'

She preferred him a little crestfallen; the Howells arrogance, for the moment at least, in abeyance. 'To be truthful, I rather liked her. Miss Harding, I mean.'

'I'm not sure we should be discussing this.'

'Protecting my innocence doesn't change the facts. I admired her, a woman making her way on her own. That can't be easy. I liked her ambition.'

And her pride. She couldn't tell him that without describing Aunt Flora's show of spite in deliberately humiliating a young woman, who could not fight back without losing her means of supporting herself to pursue the acting career she was so clearly born to follow. Giselle Harding had kept her dignity, without betraying any sign of emotion. In Rachel's eyes, it was Aunt Flora who had looked small. She had felt ashamed sitting next to her, as if she agreed with every petty insult.

'I wouldn't like her to know. Louisa, I mean.'

'Do you really think she doesn't guess?'

He gave a muffled groan at that, doubling up as if punched in the stomach, the cigarette case dropping to his feet. 'It would be better if I never came back.'

'Don't say that.' She put her hand on his arm, taking pity on him at last. 'It would break Louisa's heart. You have to return. Nothing else matters, Peter, just that you survive this.'

'I can't see how I can.' His other hand found hers, like a drowning man clinging to the life raft of human warmth as the only thing left. 'I can't tell you what it's like out there in France. None of us can. It's too unbearable. Too hopeless. I never thought war was so implacable, so devoid of right or wrong. And you can't remain the same. I didn't see that until I came back this time. I feel as if my whole life has been a dream and I'm only just waking up. And so I have to make it right. I don't want to hurt Louisa, but I have to make it right. You will make her understand? If I don't come back, that is. And that I never meant to hurt her.'

'Of course I would.'

'Thank you.' His voice eased a little, from agony to regret. 'Forgive me, Rachel. I should never have bowed to my father's pressure to marry just to suit his convenience, when I knew I could never give up Giselle. I never set out to hurt Louisa. I was always so sure I could make it right, somehow, that I had all the time in the world.'

'It felt for all of us as if we had all the time in the world,' she replied gently, 'and it will again one day, when this war is over.'

'Let's hope so.' There was a bleak hopelessness to his voice that chilled her to the very core.

Their return had been noted. From inside the house she could hear her mother calling for Hannah to open the door before Miss Rachel froze out there in the dark.

'You will explain, if I can't?' said Peter, low and urgent, as the tap of footsteps on the hall tiles rapidly approached.

'Yes, of course.' It was all she could do as he headed back towards a hell she had so recently glimpsed, in the traumatised silence of her passengers, but still knew she could not even begin to imagine.

'Thank you. And I hope Louisa can find it in her heart to forgive me. Tell her it's all I wished for. Nothing else matters. Nothing. Not any more.'

Chapter Four

'Is it true?' demanded Aunt Sara as Jess returned wearily home from the forge one evening a few weeks later.

'It must be. It was all round the harbour this morning, and Mrs Bellamy wasn't there with the rest of the charity ladies rolling bandages in the church hall.'

'Poor woman. To lose one son in a senseless accident, and now this. It must be more than she can bear. And heaven knows what will happen to the harbour now.'

'The harbour?' Jess stared at her. The day had been filled with sadness for the cheerful young man who she had seen so often over the years talking to Dad and the fishermen; who had been so full of life she could not imagine it stilled forever in the mud of a foreign field.

'With Mr Oliver gone, it will be Peter Howells who'll take over the running of the harbour when Mr Bellamy can no longer manage.'

'Howells seems decent enough,' remarked Dad, arriving behind Jess.

'But he's not a Bellamy.' Aunt Sara's thin face was taught. 'He'll see the harbour as purely a matter of business. And you can bet he'll rope in that brother of his, who'll see things in just the same way.'

'Tobias is still young.'

'He won't be for ever. And what with the two of them working together, Mrs Bellamy and Miss Rachel will easily be overruled. It's profit that will count. Look around you, Tom. The Leviathan Trading Company is half the concern it used to be. It was as plain as the nose on my face when I came back. When we were young, there used to be ships going in and out of that harbour on the hour. But even before the war, there was barely a fraction of that. Plenty of companies are struggling. What happens if Leviathan crashes?'

'It won't crash. Mr Howells has a reputation as a canny businessman; he'd never have agreed to invest in Leviathan if things had been that bad.'

'Well, from where I'm standing, I'm not so sure.' Aunt Sara's voice was thin, panicky, the way she used to sound when she had first arrived back in the harbour, when she had nowhere else to go.

'Whatever happens with the harbour, you are welcome to stay, Sara, for as long as you choose. This will always be your home, as well as mine and Jess'. I won't forget what you did for Mary. Whatever I earn, we'll make it stretch.'

Aunt Sara turned away to stir the stew. 'I don't like to impose.'

'It's not an imposition. You're my sister, and besides, I can't look after Jess without you. She's growing up fast, and a girl needs a woman to guide her. Tell her things I wouldn't know how.'

'All the same, I might try doing more with my needle,' said Aunt Sara, as Jess began to slice the loaf of bread to go with the stew.

'There's no need; we have enough to live on.'

'You and Jess both work hard to keep a roof over our heads. I'd feel happier if I could contribute.' Aunt Sara's mouth tightened. 'They were all my ideas, after all, which built the fashion house in London, for all Leonard denied it when he found it convenient to get rid of me, as if I were an encumbrance rather than the source of his success. I might have been thrown over for something younger and more pliable, but I still have my ideas. I always did have an eye for the next fashion. That was my genius, as well as being able to make something look good out of whatever materials I could lay my hands on. When Leonard and I started, we were poor as church mice, but we didn't let that stop us.'

'If that's what you wish,' murmured Dad, settling down at his place at the head of the table and picking up his well-worn copy of *Great Expectations*.

'And if Jess helps me, that will teach her a useful trade.'

Jess only just managed to avoid slicing her finger with the bread knife. 'But I have a trade.'

'You have to face facts, Jess. Working as a blacksmith is never going to last, not once the war is over and the men come home and things go back to normal. And it's clear Leviathan is never going to return to the way it was before. There's fewer trading vessels taking goods all over the world, with enemy boats likely to sink them as well as the storms. The company is going to have to adapt, and who knows what it might become? Nothing is certain. If you want to earn your living, you'd be better working with clothing and fashion than metal. There'll always be plenty of that needed, war or no war.'

'Indeed,' said Dad, deep in his book.

'But Aunt Sara, I'm learning new skills, proper metalwork, with silver and copper. I know being a blacksmith won't last for ever, but if I can mend watches and create jewellery, I'll still have a way of making a living.'

Aunt Sara snorted. 'If you want to earn a living, then you need a skill people want. Who will employ a female metal-worker?'

'There was at least one female silversmith working in St Ives before the war.'

'With a rich family and an allowance to support her, no doubt. Like half those artists who used to spend their time idling on the cliffs. They might have looked as if they lived on nothing, but they had good homes to go back to if they didn't succeed in selling their work. It makes a difference. And it's a luxury neither you nor I can afford. I dread to think what might have happened to me if I hadn't a brother to turn to for help when I was at my lowest. Sewing is a skill you can always use. Armies will always need uniforms. Men will always need suits, rich women will always require gowns. You don't want to end up a maid of all work at the big houses in St Ives, do you?'

'But I don't have the skills.'

'You can learn. With patience and application, you'll find you can learn anything.' Aunt Sara gave the stew a final stir and began ladling it into the waiting bowls. 'I'll start teaching you tonight. I learnt the hard way to look out for myself. No one else will do it. You'll thank me for this, one day; you'll see. This way you will always be able to earn some money, you'll never be totally dependent on a husband. And when the time comes, make sure you're sensible and keep a sum hidden away. Don't you be a trusting fool, like I was, without even the means to pay a solicitor. Men only think of themselves. They have all the earnings, so all of the power. You don't want to spend your life in the background, doing all the hard work, using all your energies and skills, just to be got rid of when it suits them.'

'No, Aunt Sara.' The bitterness in her aunt's voice was as harsh as fingernails on the school blackboard. Jess winced. She had caught a glimpse of the fragility beneath her aunt's determined surface. Dad, who wanted nothing more than a quiet life and the peace of his own fireside, once he had finished his responsibilities as harbourmaster for the day, was even deeper in the world of his beloved Mr Dickens.

'I spent half my life building up his tailoring business,' continued Aunt Sara. 'He never credited me with anything, but one day he'll find I was the one who made it work.'

'Couldn't you set up again, Aunt?'

'You need money for that. You need a place to greet clients, and materials to make things before you start. How's the likes of me going to afford to rent a shop in St Ives, let alone stock it?'

'There are shops empty around the harbour.'

'That's true.' Dad looked up. 'The rents are all very low; the Bellamys haven't put them up for years, and they aren't likely to. They know how much so many of the businesses are suffering from the war.'

'The harbour is hardly the place for fine tailoring,' said Aunt Sara.

'Louisa Bellamy loves fine clothes,' said Jess. 'She was always wearing something new before she married, and now she's a Howells she has plenty of money.'

Aunt Sara shuddered fastidiously. 'I dread to think who makes those things she wears – there's no skill in them at all.'

'Morwenna says it's a dressmaker in London. Her cousin Hannah has just started as a maid for the Bellamys and whenever the Howells go to their London house, Louisa comes back with something new, even now. Rich people can still buy things, Aunt Sara, and there are still dinners and parties in London. Hannah says Mrs Howells won't use a local dressmaker in St Ives – she thinks they won't be up with the latest fashions and she'll only use the London one she had when she was a girl.'

Aunt Sara sniffed. 'I'm not surprised. The creature who

makes those monstrosities is clearly still living in the time of the old queen. I'd have thought a London dressmaker would have had more sense, instead of those fussy, old-fashioned things, badly cut and badly finished. It's a shame to see them on such a pretty young woman. I could do far better than that.'

'And they have rich friends in St Ives. Hannah's always having to run around after them if they come to Enys Hall and act as their chaperone, even if they just go out for a walk along the sands.'

'This Hannah sounds like a proper gossip,' said Aunt Sara. A thoughtful look had come over her face. 'We'll see. We'll start with mending, and move on from there.'

Jess focused on buttering her slice of bread, keeping her expression hidden. She'd always sworn to herself that she was never going to be a maid like Hannah and so many of the girls from the harbour, who were employed for long hours on abysmal pay, with no time or energy for themselves. Such work was only ever seen as temporary, for the few years before they married and settled down to have their own families. Some moved to St Ives, but mostly women stayed no more than a few doors away from where they had been born.

She shut her eyes. The feeling that had overwhelmed her on the cliffs, that evening she had returned the silver hair clasp to Mrs Bellamy, was still there. She wanted more.

But Aunt Sara was only telling her what everyone would say – that one day, the war would be over and life would return to the way it had always been. As it was, most of her earnings went into the family pot to make sure the rent was covered and there was enough to pay for food, with the rest to keep her in underwear and the occasional new coat or pair of boots. Working for Mrs Wilkes had at least allowed her to do something different, and while Ben was there she had the chance to learn everything she could about metalwork, with the hope of working with him as his business expanded, or even gaining the skills to set up on her own.

There was no point in fighting Aunt Sara, for now at least. Girls like her didn't work in silver, or create necklaces and earrings for fine ladies. The only way she was going to be able to persuade anyone was by creating pieces of jewellery so beautiful, so unlike any other, that women would clamour to buy everything she made.

For that she needed time to gain the skill, and, she admitted regretfully, a way of making sure she could support herself if Mrs Wilkes was no longer able to employ her. She might not have much taste for sewing, but anything was better than having every moment of her day taken up with cleaning and polishing up at the big house, until she dropped.

As she made her way out into the yard later that evening to use the privy, and put off for a few minutes longer her aunt's insistence that they could start that evening, she looked up at the shadow of Enys Hall, a dark silhouette against the milky sheen of stars. She dreaded to think of the grief contained within its walls. Hannah was certain the news had broken the family. She said Mrs Bellamy could barely speak, while Mr Bellamy had sat for hours on Mr Oliver's favourite bench overlooking the harbour, not moving, refusing any offer of a coat to ward off the swirls of rain racing in from the sea, until Miss Rachel had managed to persuade him to take to his bed, with a fever already ravaging the old man's body and mind.

Around her, the harbour was silent. Aunt Sara was right. It wasn't just the loss of a popular young man; it was also that, for as long as anyone could remember, there had always been a Bellamy in charge of the little community. They might grumble at the price of rents, as well as the lack of sufficient maintenance of the buildings and the harbour wall these past years, but the Bellamys offered security and the reassurance that things would remain as they had always been. That hadn't changed, even with the war; it had remained the continuity that promised life would one day return to normal. Now it never would.

As she returned to the cottage, she could feel the unease lingering around the cooking fires of the darkened houses. The future of the harbour and Enys Hall now lay with Peter Howells, and Miss Louisa had always been a pliable little thing. As the prettiest and sweetest-tempered young lady this side of Plymouth, that might once have endeared her to the community, but now it marked her out as a wife unlikely to have any influence over her husband. Change was in the air, even profounder than the war itself. After the grief and uncertainty of the past years, it felt as if, regardless of what might happen in the wider world, an entire way of life was ending.

Jess tried to push the unease from her mind as she returned inside the cottage, where her aunt was waiting.

As she'd suspected, it was hemming Aunt Sara had in mind. Small, neat stitches, long lines of them, both precise and tedious, turning a much longer dress from the second-hand clothing stall in St Ives into one fit for everyday wear.

Jess worked all through the rest of that evening, as the fire crackled and the lamp began to burn down until her eyes ached and she'd stabbed herself more times than she could remember. Dad remained absorbed in his book, glancing up every now and again in an approving manner. On the other side of the fireplace, Aunt Sara was deep in forming a new dress from material taken from two second-hand skirts picked up cheap from the market.

Jess gritted her teeth. So long as Aunt Sara didn't expect her to spend all her time sewing, there were worse things. And it wasn't as if it would be for ever. She just had to be practical and sensible for now. It was the only way of keeping her dream alive.

Chapter Five

She couldn't stay. She couldn't be here a moment longer.

Rachel strode along the cliffs above the harbour, thankful to escape Enys Hall for a few minutes at least. Grief tugged at her, along with an even deeper despair. Only the exertion of her body and the feel of the wind pummelling her face gave her any sense of being alive.

In the weeks since the news of Oliver's death, she had been too consumed with her own anguish and that of her parents to think of anything else. But now the first shock had passed, and Papa had been pronounced to be out of any danger from his rheumatic fever, her sense of survival had reasserted itself.

It had been Louisa arriving in state that morning, to remain until Peter next returned on leave, which had jolted her out of her torpor. Even in the midst of shared sorrow, there had been a subtle shift in the way Louisa was greeted, a particular care that she should be comfortable and have everything she needed. Even Hannah – who had a touch of rebellion she knew she could get away with, given there was not a maid to be had this side of Truro – had bobbed with deference.

Mrs Howells. That was Louisa now. On her previous visits she had still been referred to as 'Miss Louisa', the daughter of the house she had always been. With Oliver's death, that had all changed. The agreement at the time of her marriage, the condition for the Howells to invest a proportion of their wealth into the harbour, meant that it was now Louisa's husband who was the future.

The partnership between the two families, cemented by marriage, had set out that Peter and Oliver would take control of the harbour between them. With no male Bellamy heir, it would now be Peter who would take change once Papa grew too frail, passing it down to the son he and Louisa would produce at some point, if not started already.

That side of things hadn't even been in Rachel's consideration until that morning. Despite her tears, there had been a proprietorial air about her sister as she had stood in the hallway while her trunks had been taken up to her rooms by the Howellses' manservant, sent along with the chauffeur for the purpose. At least the Howells hadn't sent Louisa's superior-looking maid, whose manner always put Hannah and Cook's noses out of joint and would have been likely to send Hannah flouncing off in a huff to the nearest munitions factory.

Louisa was clearly assuming she would be the next mistress of Enys Hall. A new future had appeared in front of Rachel, one in which she would always be the dependent spinster of the household. Aunt to her sister's children. Nurse to her mother in her old age, with no hope of any future of her own. She and Oliver had always understood each other. She'd always been confident that, even if her brother married, Enys Hall would be a secure home where she could follow her interests and live her life as she chose. That would not be the same with a Howells in charge, while Louisa had loved to lord it over her as the pretty one of the family and the one who had found a husband with ease.

Rachel had the horrible sense of a future of petty humiliations looming, with no say over her life. She'd seen the fate

53

of elderly spinsters, invisible in the background, their lives taken up with nursing young and old but regarded by those who benefited from their attentions as being of no use at all. Besides, Tobias Howells was bound to join his elder brother in running the harbour, and he had never made any secret of viewing her with the utmost disdain, as having reached the ripe old age of twenty-six without being able to secure a husband.

She shuddered. Tobias had a way of constantly reminding her that she was a failure, not a real woman at all. She had a feeling he enjoyed the subtle little digs that passed unnoticed in family conversation. It always seemed to increase his sense of power, as if it made him more of a man and kicked his own failures into the long grass, never to be seen again. He was clearly already attempting to emulate his father, who demonstrated his power by an air of superiority over his fellow man, with no need for any consideration of women at all.

Then there was Peter, who might already be regretting the vulnerability he had revealed, not to mention the existence of a mistress that he might, in times of peace, fear she could use against him.

Never trust a Howells, Cook had muttered in an unguarded moment not long before Louisa's marriage. Rachel had laughed it off at the time. But since she had come to know her new family better, she had begun to wonder about gossip that flew around the little harbour that had given Cook her jaundiced view. The tiny community had enough links with families in St Ives to know everything worth knowing, with few secrets ever escaping attention.

She had to get away. At least give herself a chance of creating her own life while her allowance was not in Louisa's gift. As soon as she could, she would find an excuse to walk to St Ives. She had friends there working for the war effort, who were always looking for ambulance drivers to volunteer to go to France. She was old enough now – no one could prevent her. Even if Papa stopped her allowance, she would have a roof over her head, she wouldn't be forced to come crawling back.

The idea had first entered her mind when she had driven the survivors from the shipwreck up to Enys Hall. Then it had seemed daunting. Now she was certain.

'I don't even care if I live or die,' she thought. 'And at least I'll be doing something useful.'

Besides, if she lived, she might at least have proved her worth and made new friends who could assist her in finding a way of supporting herself once the war was over. She didn't care what she did. Anything was better than being trapped as the poor relation for the rest of her life.

Mind made up, she turned on her heel and strode back towards Enys Hall.

Over the next weeks, as Rachel headed out to France in an ancient ambulance filled with bandages and medicines and as many fresh vegetables as the local kitchen gardens could spare, Jess continued with her work at the forge. Every day she made certain to snatch a few hours to learn from Ben, followed by evenings sewing for Aunt Sara. She was dog-tired for most of the time; but then they all were, with so many men away, and those who were left trying to keep up with all the work that needed to be done, let alone the ever-present fear of the telegram boy with dreaded news from the front.

But it was worth it. As her skill with metalwork grew, Ben finally began to teach her how to work with enamel. As well as painting with the molten glass to form images, she began to grasp the delicate art of *cloisonné*, forming patterns on the surface of the metal with thin ribbons of wire to separate the different-coloured enamels. This was followed by *champlevé*, with its patterns etched into metal to be filled with colour. She was frustrated at the clumsiness of her first attempts, but she persevered, gradually feeling the metal begin to obey the pictures in her mind.

'There are still ladies who can afford such things,' said Ben, one evening. 'Funny how life goes on as normal, even in the midst of war. It's time you and Morwenna began to take over and complete my commissions.'

Jess looked up at his tone.

'Ben's volunteered,' said Morwenna, deep in polishing a *cloisonné* pendant of lilies of the valley set against a deep green.

'You're joining the army?'

He shook his head, concentrating on finishing a brooch decorated with violets and primroses, ordered last week as a keepsake from an officer to his wife as he returned to the front. 'I said I won't fight, and I meant it.'

'He's joining the Quakers from St Ives. They're looking for volunteers to act as stretcher-bearers,' said Morwenna, blinking back tears.

'So you'll be in amongst the fighting?'

'Don't.' Morwenna winced. 'I can't bear to think of it.'

'I can't stay here and do nothing and I can't in all conscience go back to teaching jewellery-making. It's been on my mind since those refugees arrived.'

'You helped look after Frank and Charlotte, and getting them settled in St Ives,' said Morwenna fiercely. 'Isn't that something? There are still refugees arriving. You could help them.'

'I'm sorry, Morwenna, but it's not enough. I can't just do

what I can here, especially now Mum's got you and Jess. I'll be helping to save lives where it's needed most. They say the men out there on the front line are in a terrible state. The least I can do is to alleviate their suffering.'

They were quiet for a while, concentrating on finishing the work at hand, with little time for conversation. In any case, what was there to be said? Morwenna struggled to keep back her tears, while Jess stared down at her work, emptiness opening up inside her. So much for her carefully worked out plans, and now she might never see Ben again.

'That's enough for tonight,' said Ben at last. 'I can finish these before I go. It's nearly dark – I'll walk you home, Jess.'

'There's no need.'

'I'd like to.'

They slipped on their coats and walked out into the soft ending of the day.

'You'll still continue, I hope,' he said, as they reached the quay. 'Morwenna is taking over some of my commissions. I've every intention of returning and I don't want to lose all my work entirely. If you can help her, you can continue to learn.' They stopped at the harbour wall, unnoticed in the darkness, with lights still carefully doused for fear of German submarines watching from beneath the waves and Zeppelins from above. 'This has to end some time, Jess. There has to be a future. And then all the skills you're learning will find a place, just you see. I know your dad and your aunt don't want to see you disappointed, but don't let them stop you. You follow your dream. I know you too well, Jess, I know you'll never be happy in any other way. So don't throw it away to fulfil the expectations of others. Promise me you'll continue to help Morwenna?'

'Yes, of course.'

'And that you'll keep on learning and practising and making those designs of yours?'

'As much as I can.'

'You can, Jess. I've already taught you much of the basic skills; the rest you can work on for yourself. Dad was right, you know. You have a knack, a gift. And an eye for design.' His voice was wistful. 'Much of that can't be taught, I've found. Either you have it or you don't. And then it can only reach its true potential by a passion and application. You have that, Jess. Far more than many of my pupils in the School of Jewellery. You have to continue, whatever happens.'

'Then I will.'

He gave a wry kind of laugh. 'It has to be for you, Jess, not just because it's what I want, or anyone else, for that matter.'

'But it is what I want. It's what I've always wanted. I can't explain it to Dad and Aunt Sara, they just think I'm dreaming of being something I could never be. But it isn't that, it's a feeling deep inside. It's how I make sense of the world.'

'I know how you feel. That's how I see it too.' There was a moment's silence. She couldn't imagine him not being there. Fear flickered. Maybe he would never return to the harbour, even once the fighting ended. Why would he, when he had a place teaching in a respected school of jewellery, where he could follow his passion without having to supplement his income by mending gates and welding the rusting under-carriages of motorised vans? She couldn't imagine carrying on without his presence in the little workshop. She wanted to keep him there for ever.

'I will be back, Jess, and one day I won't be in the position of your teacher, or you my pupil.' He hesitated, but whatever he was about to say was lost, as a group of fishermen approached, their laughter loud in the night air. 'Come on, I'd better take you home.'

He was gone within the week.

Jess continued to work in the forge with Mrs Wilkes, slipping into the workshop whenever she could. It felt empty without Ben. Unless he was teaching her a new process, he had been quiet, concentrating on his own work. She hadn't realised how much his presence, and the intensity of his concentration to achieve perfection, had permeated the little workshop. Now they had to content themselves with infrequent letters to his mother, short and to the point and not really telling them anything at all.

'I know he can't say where he is,' said Mrs Wilkes gloomily, as summer arrived. 'But I wish he'd say that the hospital ain't anywhere near the fighting. I daren't read a newspaper, and I don't want to hear what anyone's saying.'

'What he isn't saying is that it's probably a field hospital,' said Morwenna, as she and Jess made their way to the workshop. 'Which means it could be very close to the fighting. Mum knows Ben isn't the kind to stay well back when there's men suffering.'

'No,' said Jess. She picked up a necklace she was altering for one of the families along the coast, without the heart to make a start on the intricate work.

'I wish he hadn't gone,' sighed Morwenna. 'Especially now. I know it's selfish, but a commission came through yesterday for a headband and matching pendant. It's for an original piece, to be worn by a bride for her wedding. Ben would have made exactly what they wanted.'

Jess put down the necklace, the old excitement flickering. 'There's no reason why we shouldn't fulfil the commission.'

'It looks very complicated. And they'll be expecting a really high standard of work.'

'We could at least try.' If things went wrong, it might still be a little unnerving not to be able to ask Ben, but on the other hand, she was beginning to enjoy the freedom. It felt disloyal, but it was there. Ben had been right when he said she knew much of the basics and the rest was practice and pushing herself, working things out as she went along.

In the weeks since he had left, she had begun to find her own ways of doing things. Even the designs she drew up in every spare moment were growing more adventurous as she began to explore the possibilities of the metalwork, using all her skills as a blacksmith to judge the way different metals could be beaten and shaped.

'I'm not sure.' Morwenna bit her lip. 'I feel we should turn it down and explain. Plenty of businesses have men at the front. They won't hold it against us.'

'We can explain Ben is serving his country, but that his assistant can work on it instead. They're bound to assume it's a man and we don't have to tell them it's two women.'

'But they want enamelling. They've sent an example of the kind of thing they are looking for.'

'Let me see?' The paper was of good quality, heavy, with a deeply embossed address. 'It's from London.'

'That's what I mean. They must be amazingly rich. They said Ben was recommended to them by the Birmingham School of Jewellery as being one of the best metalworkers in the country. I can't lose him their custom.'

Jess examined the sketch. 'You can easily make the pendant; you've done them before. I'll help you. And I'm sure I can work out a way to make the headband and the enamelling. They've only given a brief idea of the pattern they want, but I'm certain I can work something out around it.'

Morwenna took the paper, a touch of panic on her face. 'I know you are good, Jess. But this is a really important client.'

'All right.' Jess considered this. 'Then we could send them

an example first. We've still got enough metal and ground glass in different colours to take a chance. If I do a design and make it up, then they can approve or disapprove. We can tell them Ben is serving his country, but at least they'll see an example of our work. If they choose someone else, Ben would have lost their custom anyhow.'

'It might work.'

'What have we to lose?'

Slowly, Morwenna nodded. 'The truth is, Jess, we could really do with a commission like this, one that would pay well. Mum's finding less and less work coming into the smithy, now things are getting tighter.'

'I'm afraid so,' sighed Jess. These days there was now barely enough work to keep her at the forge at all, which had meant Aunt Sara pressing more hemming on her whenever she returned home early, or on the days Mrs Wilkes could not afford to pay her.

Sara had recently insisted on Jess learning to use an ancient treadle sewing machine she'd managed to locate. Jess was getting the hang of pressing down with her foot so that the needle shot through fabric faster than she could keep up with feeding the material through. It could finish a hem more quickly, and put together a tighter seam, than could ever be done by hand. The trouble was, being able to work at such a speed meant that Aunt Sara expected more to be done in the time, forcing her to concentrate for dear life, or at least fingers.

If she and Morwenna were able to earn money from making new necklaces, as well as the small amount Morwenna was making from continuing Ben's trade in mending clocks and broken pieces of jewellery, she might be able to prevent Aunt Sara from insisting it would be more profitable if she joined her full time in creating tucks and invisible seams and spent her days bent over her needle.

If they secured Ben's commission, she and Morwenna might have a chance of the little business being able to support them, and Mrs Wilkes too, and she could argue that it would be worth her while carrying on to secure even larger pieces. If they didn't, she could see herself slipping further and further away from the forge, to spend every waking hour working for Aunt Sara. She might never have a chance to do metalwork, let alone enamelling, ever again.

'We'll manage it,' she said firmly. 'We can do it. Just you see.'

Chapter Six

Jess spent as much time as she could working on ideas for the pendant with Morwenna, and every other spare moment on creating an elegant headband and a design for the enamelling. It was odd, the way some lives went on as if there was no war. The family who had ordered the jewellery was wealthy, the groom working in a reserved occupation, the bride nursing wounded soldiers at a London hospital. The ceremony was to be simple, but the bride had asked for something special, something unique.

The trouble was, everything Jess tried didn't quite work. It might be a wedding, but what she made could not appear frivolous, not with the war. On the other hand, it couldn't be gloomy; there was enough of that about as it was. The instructions also sent a clear request that it should be the kind of ornament its owner would be able to continue to wear on social occasions.

Her pencil kept on returning to the silver clasp that had once so entranced her, with its secret mechanism that allowed the enamelled swallow to be detached and worn in different ways. Something like that would be perfect. But maybe not so ornate. Even in the harbour, Jess could see that the way women dressed had changed. Less fussy and more practical. More functional and streamlined, with some of the girls helping on the local farms even seen to wear trousers – sending more than one of the old men nursing their pints outside the Mermaid of a summer's afternoon to shake their heads over the imminent arrival of Sodom and Gomorrah.

Finally, her pencil flew confidently across the page. As if out of nowhere, a design appeared, using interlocked ovals of yellow and green, inset with tiny *cloisonné* bees in dusky red, their outstretched wings touching, so that they looked from a distance to form an abstract pattern. The next challenge was to make it so beautifully finished that the family would be bound to commission the final piece despite knowing of Ben's absence.

It took several tries, but finally it was there. She couldn't match the experience of the maker of the swallow that had first fired her passion, but finally she had a silver hair clasp, the front piece constructed so that it could be taken apart and worn tied around the hair with a ribbon to form the requested headband, or pinned to the front of a dress as a brooch.

'Oh my goodness, that's exquisite,' exclaimed Morwenna, watching as Jess finished the polishing. 'And very clever. You can't tell just looking at it that it's in sections, and it feels perfectly secure. And yet it makes sense as a brooch.'

'It's not perfect.'

'Ben always says a design will never be perfect. It's original, and it's stunning and that's what counts.'

The next day, they carefully parcelled up the enamelled piece, along with the drawings of the final design. With the package sent, all they could do was wait.

A week passed, then another, but with no sign of any reply. Slowly, Jess began to resign herself to the design not being considered suitable, or that it was Ben's work the bride had wanted.

'But at least we had the experience,' she said one afternoon, as she joined Morwenna in the workshop. 'We managed to complete something that was beautiful. Even if this one hasn't been successful, we've proved to ourselves that we can make new things, rather than just the mending to keep the business going until Ben returns. We could try and get another commission, maybe for a less complex version of the hair clasp, at least to start with.'

'That would help Mum. She's really worried about how we are going to afford coal this winter.'

'Then we could try contacting some more of Ben's clients, and there may be families in St Ives who can still afford to buy something new, especially if it's unusual.'

'That's true,' said Morwenna. She held one of Jess' early trial pieces in her hand. 'You've got a real flair for this, more than I'll ever have. I enjoy some of it, but I don't have the passion. Not like you.'

'I don't know nearly enough,' sighed Jess. 'And I'm not sure I could ever earn a living competing against the best jewellers in London.' She took a deep breath. 'But I'm going to at least give it a try.'

The trouble was that, despite starting up a new business at such a time, Aunt Sara was soon earning enough to set up a small sewing room in one of the empty shops on the quayside, where she could work free of the dirt of the fire and the smells of cooking.

With more work coming her way, she insisted that Jess join her for longer hours, reducing even more the time in the workshop. At least Aunt Sara's reputation was growing. Already some of the wealthier ladies from St Ives were choosing to give her their custom, particularly when it came to refashioning old gowns from before the war to make them seem a little less as if they came from a bygone age, and reworking faded curtains and bedspreads to make them appear as new.

Some days, Jess began to despair of ever finding enough time to create new pieces of jewellery, let alone attempt to sell them. But once she was back in the workshop, however tired, however much her eyes and fingers ached, the old feeling came back, renewing her determination.

It was as she was stretching her aching back one afternoon, after hours of feeding heavy satin – once a voluminous ball gown complete with the most outrageous bustle she had ever seen, from which Aunt Sara was now creating a summer coat – that she found Morwenna standing on the quayside, beckoning urgently.

'I'll be back in a minute, Aunt Sara,' she called, grabbing her coat and racing out before Sara could object. 'Is it Ben?'

'Ben's well – Mum had a letter from him this morning.' Jess could have hugged her in relief. Bad news from the front was always the first thing in anyone's mind. 'Well, don't you want to know?'

'Know?' Now she looked more closely, Morwenna's face was beaming. The knot was back in her stomach again, but this time it was not dread but excitement.

'It's from London. We got the commission for the clasp after all.'

'We got it?'

'Yes! At least you did. They want some changes to the design – that's what took so long – but they loved your enamelling.'

'But that's part of the overall design.'

'And they loved it so much, they want it to be featured more on the central section, and to add a belt.'

'A belt?' Jess stared at her in alarm.

'A buckle, I think is what they mean. To match.'

'But I've never made a buckle.'

'You've worked out plenty of the rest, and Mum is bound to know. It's the enamelling that's the important part.'

'Let me see?' Jess took the paper in her hands. The sketch was rough and clumsy, but it was enough to give her an idea of the bride's request. Her fingers itched to start working out the practicalities of the buckle and to improve the design of the clasp.

Terror shot through her. Supposing she failed? She took a deep breath. She had got them into this. Besides, she wasn't going to fail. Whatever it took, she would succeed. Especially as this might be her only chance to prove herself and attract other clients.

She looked back at the sketch. There was a confidence in the looseness of the bride's drawing that Jess would under-stand, along with a trust had she could create magic. All right, so she could. After all, this was what she had dreamed of for most of her life. She wasn't about to fail now.

'We are going to need to work every hour we can,' frowned Aunt Sara, when Jess rushed up to the sewing room with Morwenna to break the news. 'I'm not sure I can spare you. I'm proud that you have secured a commission, Jess, but an order for a clasp and a buckle is hardly going to give you enough to live on.'

'But it may lead to something more,' said Jess. 'A bride is always the centre of attention, and there are bound to be wealthy guests at the wedding.'

'Artistic types,' put in Morwenna, gazing innocently at the ceiling. 'The kind who prefer something original to ones dripping with diamonds.'

'It is elegant,' admitted Aunt Sara, her eyes returning to the sketch.

'And if this works, why shouldn't we sell jewellery to match the gowns we make,' put in Jess quickly. 'All I need are offcuts of metal and ground glass. Or I could even rework unfashionable and broken pieces, like you can work miracles with whatever the moths have left.'

'Well, now, that is an idea. It would be a selling point and most women I know need a little cheering up and a touch of normality these days.' Jess could hear Aunt Sara was wavering. 'But I'm not still sure I can afford to give you time to complete this, not when my own business is starting to take off.'

'I'll work all the hours I can for you, Aunt Sara.'

'And I can sew,' volunteered Morwenna. 'I can take over some of Jess's work while she's finishing the commission.'

'I need someone who can use a treadle machine.'

'Oh, that's easy. I've used Mum's since I was a little girl. Mum hates sewing, but to be honest I sometimes prefer it to working with metal.'

'Well...'

'And I can embroider,' said Morwenna. 'That's my real skill. And smocking. Most of the children in the harbour are dressed in my smocking.'

'Embroidery...' Aunt Sara's eyes focused on the delicate form of a shell etched into the collar of Morwenna's coat. 'Is that your work?'

'And on the cuffs.' Morwenna held out the pattern of shells skilfully drawing the eye away from the worn and much-mended edges. 'I can't bear things to be plain. These are ones I've done ages ago, I've made much better patterns since.'

'I'd never thought of trying to find anyone skilled in embroidery in the harbour. I don't have the patience myself, but I had a team of embroiderers in London. It can give such a unique touch to a garment. Can you work in silk?'

Morwenna swallowed. 'I'll make sure I can.'

There was a moment's silence. Jess held her breath. Finally, Aunt Sara nodded. 'Very well. I'm prepared to give it a try. But your mother must agree to it first, Morwenna. And just this once, Jess. Unless you are inundated with commissions, that is. Then I might possibly reconsider.'

'Yes, Aunt Sara,' said Jess meekly. The moment she'd finished the pieces for the bride, she would work day and night on securing other commissions. She didn't have the means to make expensive pieces to see if they would sell, but commissions would work. And in between she could use offcuts of metal and anything she could lay her hands on to create brooches and earrings. Maybe even a simpler version of the hair clasp. If her designs could sell to a wealthy woman in Kensington, she could surely sell them elsewhere. She might never have to sew another seam again.

Bursting with excitement, she accompanied Morwenna down the small flight of steps to the door.

'I can't wait to tell Ben,' said Morwenna. 'He'll be incredibly proud of us managing to secure that commission. And probably more than a little envious.'

'We won't let him down,' said Jess, hugging her. 'I wish I could start this minute, but I'd better get back to Aunt Sara. The last thing we need is for her to change her mind.'

Morwenna was no longer listening. Her attention was focused on a small crowd gathering in the harbour. As Jess watched the crowd grow, the low murmur of voices swelled ever louder.

'What on earth has happened?' called Aunt Sara, throwing open the window.

'I'm not sure.' Any hope that it might be news of the ending of the war was banished by the shaking of heads and the subdued conversations. More than one glanced up towards Enys Hall.

'Oh my lord,' breathed Aunt Sara, as Morwenna ran to find out more. They waited in silence until Morwenna returned. 'Is it Mr Bellamy?'

Morwenna shook her head. 'It's Peter Howells. He's been killed in action in France. The news came through to the family in St Ives a few hours ago. Poor Miss Louisa.'

'And they'd barely been married,' exclaimed Aunt Sara. 'Damn this war for taking the brightest and the best, and leaving so many widows. First Oliver Bellamy and now this. And old Mr Bellamy looking frailer each time I see him. Who knows what will happen to the harbour, and all of us, now.'

The mood was subdued for the rest of the day. Jess concentrated on finishing the seams of the satin coat, trying to shut out the gloom that had settled over the little community, and the worried expression on Aunt Sara's face.

Later that afternoon, as she stepped out onto the quay to follow Aunt Sara, who was already striding towards the cottage to start the evening meal, a movement caught Jess' eye. On the road above, a motor car was making its way slowly from the direction of St Ives, heading for Enys Hall.

A touch of chill prickled through her. 'Don't be an idiot,' she scolded herself. After all, there were many large black motor cars, most of which looked the same as far as she could tell, and there was no reason for this to be the very same Bentley she had seen Ben mending for Peter Howells.

As she watched, the vehicle pulled into the lay-by above the harbour. Her breath left her body as a fair-haired man stepped out, to stand there, looking down. But it was not a ghost. Nor even a miracle of mistaken identity and a man returned from the dead. He might have Peter Howell's fair hair, but even from a distance she could make out that the rest of him was smaller and slighter. There was something about the way he stood, perfectly still, hands in pockets, watching the quiet industrious bustle of the harbour, that sent an uneasy finger snaking down her spine.

His head turned a little. Instinctively, she stepped back into the shadow of the doorway, certain he had caught her watching him. She cursed under her breath. She had a feeling, deep in her bones, that the less she intruded on the man's notice, the better. He remained perfectly still for a moment. Then he returned to the Bentley, turning round impatiently in the narrow space, before racing back in the direction of St Ives.

Part Two

—

1920

Chapter Seven

'Surely there has to be some boat returning to St Ives today?'

Jess turned towards the unfamiliar voice, clutching her hat as the wind swept across the bay, bringing with it the mist of spray from waves breaking high against the harbour wall.

Since the ending of the Great War over a year ago, there hadn't been many strangers among the tiny cluster of cottages around the harbour, even at the height of summer. Particularly not young men of the well-dressed variety, whose boots alone must have cost more than the fishermen mending nets on the quay could hope to earn in a year.

'I'm afraid not, sir,' replied Dad. 'This is a private harbour. There's not much call for boats to and from St Ives, you'll find. But the walk along the coast is very pleasant, especially with the day so fine. It won't take long.'

'It seems I have no choice.' The stranger settled back to dabbing paint on the canvas set in front of him on the harbour wall. Jess could see why he didn't sound too pleased at the prospect of a walk, however short, carrying his easel and folding stool, not to mention his canvas and an extensive collection of paints and brushes. The wind ruffled his dark hair, sending strands across his face. He pushed them back absently, revealing the missing fingers on his left hand.

Jess sighed and continued on her way, taking the flask of hot soup to her father in the harbourmaster's office.

'Thank you, sweetheart. I was ready for that.' Jess reached

for two bowls from the shelf on the wall, along with a small butter dish.

'And there's cheese, I nearly forgot.' Jess fished for the small slab she had picked up at the grocer's, sitting with the vegetables for tonight's stew.

'Give me a minute.' Dad's attention was back on the painter, a thoughtful expression on his face. 'He must have money, that one. Been an officer in the war, I should think. He must have some private means, having the leisure to paint all day, and that suit can't be more than a few months old. I thought all these artists coming here were claiming to be as poor as church mice.'

'Maybe not all of them.'

'No, indeed.' Dad scanned the small collection of boats in the harbour, his gaze alighting on Fred Williams, who was cleaning the family's small boat with vigour. The painter was following Fred's every move, having clearly settled on the neatest and most picturesque of the boats as worthy of his interest. 'If he can pay good money, I don't see why he shouldn't have his fill of all the scenery he could desire. And Fred always could talk the hind leg off a donkey.'

Jess watched him make his way over to where Fred's boat was moored, followed by their heads coming together, deep in conversation. Fred didn't take much persuading. Jess suppressed a smile as Dad strolled back to the artist, who looked delighted at whatever extortionate price Dad and Fred had cooked up between them to take him on the short journey back to St Ives as soon as the tide was right.

Dad returned with a satisfied gleam in his eye. 'If St Ives can make a living from artists, I don't see why we shouldn't,' he remarked. 'Time some prosperity came here.' He reached for the butter dish and the remains of a loaf from a shelf above his desk. 'No work this afternoon?'

Jess shook her head. 'Aunt Sara finished her last two orders early. Several more came in before we left, so she's stayed to reply to them. I'm on my way to make the meal for tonight.'

'New orders, eh? So Sara was right, things are really starting to take off with the dressmaking business.'

'One of them is from an emporium on Oxford Street, in London. They've used us for small things before, but this time it's much more. They said Aunt Sara's tailoring is the best in the country.'

'Well I never.' Dad sliced cheese onto his bread. 'That must be down to you too.'

'I hope so.' She winced slightly under his pride. Dad hadn't quite been able to hide his relief that she was no longer working at the forge. It had been different during the war, but once the men returned in need of work, it had become frowned upon for women to try to cling to the positions they had filled while the emergency lasted. Besides, life was returning to normal, to just as it had always been.

Except that, of course, it never could.

Aunt Sara was a perfectionist, but for good reason. She had recognised that her enterprise was too small to compete with the large factories, and was specialising instead in high-end tailoring and exquisite embroidery. At least it had meant Morwenna was now employed on a regular basis to use her embroidery skills.

Through the window of the harbourmaster's office, Jess could see the artist on the harbour wall was back to being completely absorbed in his work, lost to everything except the canvas before him. Jess hugged herself, trying not to envy that freedom. With every last part of her being, she missed the exhilaration when all her energies were concentrated on turning an inert piece of metal into a brooch or flower, seeing it form beneath her fingers.

77

They had come so close, she and Morwenna, during those last years of the war, gradually building on the success of the headband and buckle. Bit by bit, they had attracted more commissions for brooches and pendants and even the odd buckle, right up to the last weeks before the Armistice. But then the news had come about Ben and all activity in the workshop had ceased, never to start again.

'Idiot!' Aunt Sara burst in, face scarlet with fury. 'Selfish, stupid idiot.' She banged her fist on the table, sending the soup bowls clattering.

Dad rose to his feet. 'Sara?'

'I should have known. You can think the best of everyone, Tom, but I should have known what he was up to.'

'For goodness sake, Sara, sit down, take my chair. Jess will make us a cup of tea. Who has annoyed you now?'

'Annoyed me?' Aunt Sara was livid. 'Set fair to ruin me. He knows I can't pay that kind of money. No one in the harbour can. This wouldn't have happened when Mr Bellamy was alive or if Mr Oliver had survived. It will be the cottages next, you mark my words.'

Jess's heart sank. 'You mean the rent?'

'What else?' Aunt Sara took an official-looking letter out of her pocket. 'This arrived, just a few minutes ago. It's from Tobias Howells' solicitor. The rents on all the businesses are going up by a third from next month. A third! And that will just be the start.'

Dad frowned. 'He can't do that. Mrs Bellamy will never allow it.'

'It says here that he's acting on her behalf. He's taken over Mr Peter's position, but with no Mr Oliver to look out for us. It's all been legally agreed. There's nothing we can do.'

'I'll speak to Mr Howells, Sara. Tobias is too young and inexperienced to understand that most of the businesses are just about making ends meet. This could send them all out of the harbour. It makes no business sense.'

'It'll leave the harbour empty, ready for his father to do with it as he pleases, more like. I told you this was exactly what would happen. Typical Howells tactics. How else do you think they've become so rich?'

'There are skilled workers here they won't want to lose,' reasoned Dad. 'The harbour's only just getting back on its feet after the war.'

'Since the war the Howells have concentrated on merchandise they can buy cheap and sell on at a profit, even if they have the expense of shipping it halfway around the world. Old Mr Howells so much as told me so when I tried to get him to take some of my evening gowns for his stores in America. He'd only have been interested if I could undercut his present supplier. Besides, he made it clear he won't deal with women. Considers it beneath him.'

'We'll work something out,' said Jess, handing her a cup of tea.

'The trouble is, he's clearly certain no one's going to stand against him, now it's only women left at Enys Hall.'

As her aunt continued to vent her fury, Jess escaped, muttering about needing to get to Pengelly and Sons before the last of the meat – never very plentiful with so few families being able to afford it, not even on Sundays – ran out.

As she made her way towards the little grocer's shop, it struck her again how much the harbour had changed. Even after the men had returned home from the war, it had not been the same. Like everywhere else, people just wanted to get on with their lives and forget the years of constant fear and worry, but even within the shelter of the little cove it was impossible to escape the past. She gazed up towards Enys

Hall, already beginning to appear crumbling and forlorn, ivy creeping up its walls, the garden overgrown.

Nothing could ever be the same again, she would hear the old fishermen agree, nodding together as they sat mulling over the state of the world on the harbour wall, mourning the long-gone days when the herring were plentiful and every young man followed his father on the fishing boats or the trading vessels of the Leviathan Trading Company.

'You had a letter too, then,' she said to Mrs Wilkes, who was sitting on the bench outside the forge.

'Aye.' Mrs Wilkes folded up the paper in her hands and placed it in her pocket.

'But surely they can't close the forge.'

'Not for now, at least. We're too small to be a threat to them and they still need our services, for now. And besides, they can hardly ...' She cleared her throat as Ben slowly limped his way outside, joining her on the bench. Jess still couldn't help feeling the hurt that he was still avoiding her eyes. Shutting her out, pretending she wasn't there. As if her mere presence was a painful reminder of all that he had lost.

'Who wants to close the forge, Mum?'

'No one.'

'There's really no need to protect me.'

'Truly, no one.'

'Well then, I can guess. Howells is putting up the rents for the shops and the workshops, is that it?'

'So it seems.'

Ben grunted. 'That's a predictable if short-sighted move if ever there was one.'

'Then let's hope he thinks the better of it.'

'I'm glad they're not trying to close the forge,' said Jess.

Mrs Wilkes cleared her throat. 'The trouble is, the workshop.'

'The workshop?' Ben's head shot up.

'There's no mention of it here, but they must know it's no longer in use, for now, at least, or they'd have raised the rent enough to cover it.'

'Then it's a good thing it's not,' said Ben.

Jess squashed an inward sigh. Since her last commission for a pair of enamelled earrings, during the final weeks of the war, she had ached to start on a new project. But once the news had arrived about Ben being so badly injured, followed by months when he was not expected to survive, she hadn't had the heart to intrude on Morwenna and Mrs Wilkes. Since his return it had been impossible.

'But I had hoped...' Mrs Wilkes stopped as Ben turned his face away. 'You're recovering, Ben, getting stronger every day. There are still enquiries fer commissions. You might wish to...'

'How can I?' he retorted bitterly, holding up his scarred and battered right hand. With the final bandages now removed, the stumps that were all that remained of his two middle fingers sent a jolt through Jess's belly.

'You can still teach Morwenna. And Jess too. They made some nice things while you were away. Got a few commissions of their own. If you show them, you can help them to do more.'

'It's not the same,' he muttered, pulling himself to his feet and returning inside.

'He'll find a way,' said Mrs Wilkes. 'He might not think so now, but he'll find a way of doing his work again.' Tears briefly filled her eyes, quickly blinked away. 'And I can't help being grateful fer being one of the lucky ones, for having my boy come back to me. The Howells and the Bellamys would give anything to be in my place. At least mine came home.'

'I know,' said Jess, gently squeezing the older woman's arm.

There had been weeks of agony after Ben had been caught in mortar fire while rescuing wounded from the battlefield. All any of them could do was wait while he spent all those weeks in a hospital in France, and then – once he was strong enough to be moved – in London as surgeons fought to save his right hand. 'Ben will find a way to get back to his work, I know he will.'

Mrs Wilkes patted her arm, which was the nearest thing to an expression of emotion she would allow herself. 'That's the trouble with war, fer all the government can tell us it's won and that's that. It's not a thing that can just be won or lost. You ask Mrs Howells and Mrs Bellamy, or any of the mothers with sons dead or maimed. Fer them, it'll never be over.' She glanced up towards Enys Hall, to the figure of Rachel Bellamy striding over the cliffs, heading home from the wilder reaches of the coast, as she did most mornings, always hatless, rain or shine, as if daring the sea winds to blow her into smithereens. 'Nor fer them brave souls as were out there and saw the worst of it.'

Jess followed her gaze. They had all been so grateful when the war finally ended. They had all been too weary, too worn out with loss, to celebrate, but at least there had been the feeling that the worst was over, and things might now return to the way they were before.

'I'd better get back home,' she muttered.

Mrs Wilkes blew her nose in a determined manner, eyes returning to the figure silhouetted against the sky, vanishing into the next dip on the clifftop. 'Trouble is, the Howellses already own that land on the other side of the harbour, the bit with the meadows going up towards the cliffs. Peter Howells bought it when he were first engaged to Miss Louisa, that time we were all worried the Bellamys might go bankrupt. So now all they have to do is get rid of us, let the cottages on this side go to rack and ruin, then buy them up cheap, knock them down and turn everything into storage warehouses for their export business. Bugger a business partnership – that's what old Howells wanted all along, if you ask me.'

Jess watched as Rachel continued striding towards the house. She had only returned from France a few months ago, after Mr Bellamy, who had never really recovered from the death of his remaining son, had been struck down with the lung infection that killed him. The word in the harbour was that she had been working with refugees and those so badly wounded it would be years before they could be discharged from medical care. Since her return, she had become a familiar sight, the lone woman striding across the cliffs in all weathers, as if haunted by a thousand ghosts she feared would never leave.

There were a dozen rumours flying round the cottages, as there always were, to explain a woman not acting as a woman should, even after the ravages of war. And a pity it was, Jess had heard the landlord of the Mermaid remark as she waited outside the door for Dad to join her for the walk home, Miss Rachel being the only one of them with her head screwed on. Woman or not, she'd have been the best hope they had, now the boys were gone and that young devil Tobias could do as he pleased. There had been dark mutterings of agreement among the drinkers, and even Dad had looked uneasy when he emerged, his weatherbeaten face for once without its good-humoured optimism.

Jess stopped at the harbour wall, where the high tide swelled against the protective barrier, now and again sending feathers of spray high into the air, spitting on her face.

She'd had no choice but to step back from using the workshop when all anyone could think of was willing Ben to survive and come home. Once he had returned, with injuries so severe he would never be able to resume his work, she no longer had the heart. It had seemed unfair, sacrilegious even, to continue when he had lost everything. This last year, with so little work arriving for Mrs Wilkes at the forge, and the new garage having opened up in St Ives to cater for the increasing number of motor vehicles in use, it was only Morwenna's work with Aunt Sara that was keeping the family afloat. Everyone in the harbour could see the forge would not be open for much longer, and with not enough profit in the business for anyone to take it over, it would become yet another redundant business, unable to withstand the effects of the war and the changing times.

Jess sighed in frustration. She had come so close. The delighted response to her enamelled hair clasp with its versatile design, and the buckle in the form of a bee balanced on a stylised flower, had confirmed that she had both the imagination and the skill. There had to be a way she could earn her living through her metalwork.

Over the past weeks, when several more enquiries for brooches had arrived in the post, she had begun to consider asking if she could rent the workshop from Mrs Wilkes. Especially now Ben was stronger, maybe she could also encourage him to find a way of overcoming his disability. She could sense he missed working as much as she did and she hated to see him a shadow of his former self. Sometimes it felt as if it was more than the use of his hand that he had lost in France. He felt shut away, a grief inside him that would never heal.

Thank goodness she hadn't quite yet plucked up the courage. Like many of the small businesses, it was only the meagre rent that allowed the Wilkes to survive at all. If it had been increased for the workshop, they would have been forced out for certain, and until she was able to get a steadier flow of commissions she could barely cover the cost of coal and materials.

Jess watched the shoot of spray against the cliffs beyond the harbour and the sails of the pleasure yacht caught in the sun. She pulled the small notebook from her pocket, sketching the patterns developing in her mind. She could see how they could form into the oval shape of a brooch, as clearly as if it were already in front of her; the finished suggestion of the scene, the varying hues of orange and red in the rays of the enamel echoing the reality in front of her, catching its essence.

That was the thing she had discovered since the workshop had lain idle and she'd been forced to turn commissions away. She might have told the woman who had enquired about a brooch that she wasn't able to take on commissions for now, but her mind still worked on the project all the same. She couldn't let it go.

Ideas came from everywhere, in everything she saw. The little notebook was almost filled with the curve of cottages down to the harbour and the shadows of cliffs stretching out into the distance, interspersed by wind-bent trees on the cliffs and the leap of dolphins in the bay. She hadn't the skill to capture them in fine detail, but that didn't matter. It was the lines she wanted; clear, bold lines that she could form with thin wires of copper or silver, before filling the enclosed spaces with layers of enamel, each one deepening the richness of colour.

So many of the sketches she could already see in her mind's eye as the finished piece; as brooches and earrings, as well as new versions of the headband. She worked on them in her head in the long hours of hemming and stitching for Aunt Sara, snatching every opportunity she could to sketch out the final design, complete with pins or fastenings, to hold it in her memory, ready for when she was able to start again. She already had a collection of notebooks, bought with any money she could spare and hidden under her mattress for safety, filled with designs. Try as she might to forget, the deep longing to work on them, beating and polishing until they were as perfect as could be, would not go away.

The trouble was, she couldn't bear the thought of causing Ben hurt by watching her develop the skills he could no longer physically manage. On the other hand, she knew in her bones that she couldn't just walk away and accept her life as forever being that of a seamstress.

There had to be another way. Jess pushed her most recent notebook deep into her pocket and headed for Pengelly and Sons, turning her thoughts to the preparation of tonight's stew. She didn't know how, but she was going to find a way to start again.

Chapter Eight

'Louisa!' Rachel ran up the stairs in Enys Hall two at a time, throwing open the door to her sister's bedroom in exasperation. 'It's all right, Hannah. You can leave Mrs Howells' hair. I'm sure you've plenty of other pressing tasks, without doing this. I'll finish it.'

'Yes, miss.' With an apologetic bob, Hannah shot past her and down the stairs, where, a moment later, Cook's roar could be heard greeting her in the kitchen.

'It was nearly done anyhow,' said Louisa, eyeing herself in the dressing-table mirror. 'I don't know why you always think you should interfere.'

'Couldn't you at least try to do your hair yourself? Mama and I both manage.'

'But you don't care much for your appearance. Just because I'm stuck here doesn't mean I shouldn't make an effort to look nice.'

'For heaven's sake, it's only the three of us sitting down to dinner!' Rachel caught the hurt look on her sister's face and swallowed her impatience. 'Of course I don't object to you looking pretty. But you are lovely as you are, darling, and Hannah has quite enough to do as it is.'

'She said she didn't mind.'

'We pay her wages – what else was she supposed to say?'

'There's no need to shout.'

Rachel took a deep breath. It wasn't poor Louisa's fault

that irritation had stalked every fibre of Rachel's being ever since her return from France, nerves strung taut, set jangling by even the banging of plates in the kitchen. Any more than Louisa was responsible for the emptiness of loss in her heart, or the nightmares that haunted her dreams. She tried to regain her patience.

'I'm sorry. I'm not blaming you, Louisa; it's just we can't afford to lose her.' She gathered up the abandoned twists of hair into the elaborate coil behind her sister's head, tucking them in neatly. 'Domestic servants can't be had for love nor money these days. Hannah could find a much easier job elsewhere, and especially with Cook treating her like a scullery maid on top of being expected to keep the place clean on her own.'

'It's not my fault I'm stuck here. The Howells always thought I wasn't good enough for their London set, not even during the war. They couldn't wait to see the back of me. They always made me feel like a country bumpkin.'

'You could never be that, Louisa.'

'They never wanted me to go back to them, ever. You should have heard the way they spoke of Papa, and you and Mama. As if we were all stupid. As if we didn't matter.' She burst into tears. 'I know they couldn't wait to get rid of me. It would have been different if I'd been carrying Peter's child. I should have had a wild affair and made sure I had a child, any child. That would have served them right.'

'Thank goodness you didn't. You're still young, Louisa, you've your whole life ahead of you. I know it's hard, but I'm certain that one day you'll find happiness again.'

'How am I to meet any suitable young men when you and Mama won't take me anywhere? Even St Ives is too far.'

'You can go every day if you walk.'

'You can walk if you like. You are always walking. I'm not

turning up like some hoyden and then have to walk back again. Besides, what would I do? I don't know anyone there, and I'm not going to be patronised, not for any money.'

'Then perhaps we should find a way of bringing people here.'

'Who wants to come here? With just a bunch of women and no money for anything. It would be different if Simon and Oliver were alive.'

'Don't, Louisa. Don't. They are gone, just like Papa. We can't change that. So many men were lost in the war. We're not the only ones.' She sighed. 'It might be a good thing if we are forced to move away and start again.'

'Mama will never agree to leave Enys Hall. She said so.'

'She may have no choice, Louisa. Things are pretty bad with Leviathan, you know. Even with the investment from the Howells, trade hasn't recovered since the war.'

Little enough investment, if truth were told; mainly in dredging out the encroaching silt that had prevented larger ships from entering the harbour for the previous years, nearly bankrupting the Bellamys, who by that time had not the means to complete the work.

Rachel bit back the words. Since Peter's death, there had been nothing of the promised renovations to the existing workshops, let alone the plans for increased storage and attracting new manufacturing enterprises into the workshops to make the harbour thrive once more. She had hoped the Howells had lost interest and would leave the harbour alone to carry on as best it could and find its own way to survive, just as it had always done. But it seemed not.

'Well, Tobias says...'

'Tobias! When did he get back?'

'A few days ago. He came down from London ahead of

the rest of the family. They are opening up the house in St Ives again. Didn't you know?'

'I hadn't heard.'

'The family will be starting to come down to Cornwall for the summer again, like they used to.' Louisa smoothed her brows with her fingers, the discontent in her face easing. 'Perhaps then I might have some society again. They are bound to invite me, and they have a motor car. Two, in fact. Tobias has taken over Peter's Bentley. It will be nice to be driven to places again.'

'And how do you know all this?'

'Oh, I expect someone told me.' In the mirror, her eyes met Rachel's. A slight flush rose over the delicate features. 'Tobias wrote to me. He offered to take me to the house, once the family are there. They are my family too. I would like to see them again.'

'I thought you said they couldn't wait to send you back to Mama?'

'Oh, that was in London. It won't be at all the same here. Besides, Tobias will look after me. He was always kind.'

Rachel gritted her teeth. 'I bet he was. He tried soft-soaping me once, until he realised it was of no use.'

'He said you seemed to have taken a dislike to him. He was very hurt.'

'Louisa, do you always take what every man says at face value?'

'So he was right. You don't like him.'

'Not particularly. I'm not obliged to like everyone I meet.'

'Tobias said it was because he thought you were a bit afraid of men, you know, being...' She caught the look in her sister's eyes and stumbled to a halt.

'An old maid?' put in Rachel, bluntly. 'Don't tell me. The old story of the dried-up spinster, untouched by man, waiting to be awakened in trembling anxiety for the honour of being noticed by any male.'

Louisa swung round, blue eyes narrow, mouth in a tight line. 'You said that almost as if ...'

Rachel kicked herself. Dangerous ground. She had been so careful to keep hidden the secrets of her heart, not to mention her lost innocence, ever since her return from France. She ached to confide in her mother, but, as with so much of the agony of working on the front line for months on end, she did not know where to begin. Intimate relations with a man – and especially one so unsuitable, considered so socially beneath her – would have shocked Mama.

She was ashamed to admit it, but Rachel lacked the courage to so completely defy convention, to be pointed at, laughed at, pitied as a fool too easily led to her own ruin. In the edge-of-life intensity of the field hospital she had been utterly certain of her own heart. In the cold light of everyday life, the impossibility had overwhelmed her, fracturing everything she'd ever felt or believed into a myriad of tiny pieces.

Mama had been all too eager to believe that the nurses and volunteers had lived in a state of nun-like virtue. How impossible to explain the febrile atmosphere of youth thrown so close together among so much death and suffering, when life could end at any moment, that had so easily turned a passing attraction into the passion that had consumed her, throwing all caution to the winds.

Impossible. She could not bear the thought of Mama's hurt at her recklessness. And besides, the secret was not only hers. Fear shot through her. Hadn't she caused enough harm? She would never forgive herself if she was to cause more, and to one who had lost so much already. She had to keep the secret safe. It was the only act of love she had left.

Rachel shook herself. 'That's the dinner bell. Don't worry,

Louisa, you can keep on lording it over me as a woman of the world. When did Tobias say he'd visit?'

'Tomorrow.' Rachel breathed a little easier. At least she knew Louisa well enough to know how to distract her from awkward questions and even trickier guesswork. She had learnt to her cost that Louisa was sharper than she liked to appear. If anyone was to guess the secrets she kept hidden in her heart, it would be Louisa. And Tobias was just the kind to worm such information out of Louisa to use to his advantage and for the enjoyment of watching others squirm. Her flesh crawled at the thought.

'You shouldn't be so hard on her, my dear,' said Mrs Bellamy, looking up from her lists as Rachel joined her, leaving Louisa to finish dressing. Since Papa's death, Mama had spent her days making endless lists. 'The loss of a husband is a terrible thing. It breaks a woman; you've no idea how lost she can feel without her life's companion. And Louisa always was a sensitive creature.'

'I understand what you mean, Mama, and I know how much you miss Papa. All I want is for Louisa to stop monopolising Hannah, when it's clear to all she's the only maid we have, and I doubt Louisa will want to spend all day cleaning grates if we lose her.'

'Hannah has never once talked of taking up another post.'

'That's only because her grandmother is still in one of the cottages by the harbour. The old lady's a survivor, but she can't last for ever; then Hannah will have nothing to keep her here. She won't be able to afford the rent of the cottage on her own, not with the kind of wages she earns here, and there are plenty of opportunities for a bright girl like her.'

'How do you know all this?'

'I listen, Mama. I talk to people. That's what the war taught me, working with those of all different backgrounds and classes. I learnt they were no different from us. They weren't stupid or greedy. They had dreams and ideals. And some of the factory girls I worked with driving ambulances out in France were far better educated than I'll ever be. They had been to evening classes and lectures after long hours of work, with a passion to educate themselves that made me quite ashamed. Several had worked with the suffrage movement, risking their jobs and their freedom to improve women's lives. Many were a good deal more informed than I was.'

'My dear, you sound quite alarmingly revolutionary.'

'Do I?' Rachel bent over the back of the chair to kiss her cheek. 'I'm not in the least revolutionary, Mama. I'm not single-minded enough. Believe me, those years driving an ambulance showed me enough of conflict to last a lifetime. Besides, you should hear real revolutionaries talk.'

'Rachel!'

'I'd best see how Cook is getting along,' said Rachel hastily, at her mother's scandalised expression. 'Heaven knows what we'll do when the hens stop laying. The most sensible thing would be to have a cow or two in the front gardens; at least then we might have a chance of making cheese.'

'Good grief, we had enough of that during the war. The newspapers are all filled with the country's prosperity.'

'London, maybe. But not here in Cornwall. At least not for us.'

'It would be very different if your father was alive. Or at least one of your brothers. It was very cruel of fate to take them both.'

'I know.' Rachel took the nearest hand and squeezed it gently. 'I miss them all dreadfully, too. But we aren't the only family to have suffered such a terrible loss, Mama, and the Howells lost a son, too. Somehow we all need to find the strength to carry on.'

Mrs Bellamy leant back in her chair. 'Perhaps we should see if Mr Howells will buy out the Leviathan Trading Company and the harbour. We would still have the house.'

'And nothing to support it. At least our income from the rents still allow us to survive after a fashion. What would we do without them?'

Her mother bent over her lists once more. 'We could sell the house. There is room for us with Aunt Julia now your cousins have left home. Birmingham is not the same as St Ives, and I know you would miss the sea. But it may be the only chance we have.'

'Mama...'

Mrs Bellamy put down her pencil, folding up her latest list. 'My dear, I've done the figures over and over again. However much we economise, it just won't add up. And that is without any repairs to the place. The families in the cottages are struggling as it is; I can't agree in all conscience to Tobias's suggestion that we increase their rents. The businesses are one thing; Tobias assures me the remaining businesses are doing well and the rents don't even cover the maintenance costs, and new enterprises are enquiring about renting workshops all the time. But raising the rent on the cottages makes no sense. Not in the long run. Most of the families simply won't be able to pay, and we'll be faced with the decision of whether to evict them, while others will simply leave to find work elsewhere. Far from solving our problems, it could leave us with no income at all.'

'I'm sure he'll see that you're right.'

Her mother played distractedly with the pencil in her hand. 'I'm trying to be realistic, darling, but it's everything your father worked for. His last words to me were that he was comforted by knowing that you and I would always have

94

a home, whatever happened. That was his last wish, that we would always be secure.'

Rachel frowned at her. 'Are you quite sure Tobias was right about the workshops, Mama? I can't see much evidence of new businesses attempting to come in.'

'I can't see what else we can do, especially as we can't afford to finance any repairs ourselves.' She sighed. 'It feels as if the world has passed us by and there's no place for us any more.'

'That's not true, Mama! Surely between us we can come up with a solution, one that doesn't necessarily involve the Howellses. There has to be something we can do.'

'I'm too old, my dear, and tired. All I want is a quiet life.'

'You are not old, Mama! And you can't really want to live with Aunt Julia, of all people? Who always looks down on you and barely has the time of day for me and Louisa, but now sees an opportunity to secure a nurse, three nurses, for the rest of her days. And she'll still leave all she owns to cousin Wilfred, who'll turf us all out when we are no longer of any use.'

'That is very harsh, my love. It makes you sound quite embittered.'

'Being realistic is not embittered. Can you really tell me it's not true?'

There was a moment's silence. 'There would be more society in Birmingham. There would be more chance for you and Louisa to find husbands. Louisa can't spend the rest of her life in mourning; she will only find happiness if she can become a wife and mother. At least I might see you both settled.'

'I'm not sure the young ladies of Birmingham would appreciate us arriving in an attempt to steal what few men they have left.'

'Darling, it's not a thing to joke about.'

95

'Oh, Mama. I know you're trying to think of what's best for us, but this is our home and I don't like the idea of abandoning the harbour, not until we have no other choice. It doesn't feel fair to the families who have worked so hard for us and have given us all we have. There has to be a way we can earn enough to support us. Others do.' She took a deep breath. 'In fact, the last time I walked over to St Ives, it struck me just how much it has returned to being as busy it was before the war, in fact even busier. And there are so many more artists. The papers were quite right – it's becoming quite a centre for the artistic community all year round, as well as for holidaymakers in the summer. Others are using it to make a living, so why shouldn't we? Many of the big Victorian villas on the cliffs have been turned into guesthouses and most of them said they had no vacancies.'

'We'll see.' Mama turned with a smile as Louisa appeared at the door. 'Good evening, my darling. You look lovely.'

'I'll find out how Cook is doing,' muttered Rachel, escaping down towards the kitchens. As she reached the corridor, she stopped, peering out into the garden with the blue of the sea beyond. She was itching to escape, to throw herself back into the business of the day, when there was no time to think beyond the encroachment of slugs in the kitchen garden and the vegetable patch, or organising the mending of the church roof, battered in last winter's gales and sure to fly off if left to the mercy of next autumn's storms. Her only other solace was her long tramps across the cliffs in all weathers, wearing her body out, keeping her mind closed.

Tonight, she missed Oliver more than ever. Even after all this time, and so much loss, the pain of his absence went through her. When her brothers were alive, the household had been full of noise and life, with arguments flying about politics and the best way to manage the harbour and make it thrive once more.

How little had they known. It felt like a different world. A more innocent time, when there was right and wrong and the future had been laid out, steady and clear.

In the pane of the window, her face looked back, no longer rounded and girlish, but settled into its adult form. The woman she would always be from now, haunted by the sights and smells of the battlefield that had once been beyond her darkest imagination but now would never leave her. The face lined with the anguish that wracked her body, once so warmed by love, but now cold, with no emotions left. A face that no longer knew what to feel or believe. Just a terrible emptiness hollowed out within. Sometimes, she thought she might never learn to feel again.

A flare of sunlight from behind the encroaching clouds caught her gaze, as it stretched down to illuminate the little harbour. Instantly, it was transformed from a dingy, workaday place, to a protective curve with the deep turquoise of the sea beyond. It was only after being away for so long that she had seen the familiar little cove with new eyes. She was still brought up short now and again by its beauty, like the artist on the harbour wall, who was now packing up his equipment as the light began to fade, making his way towards one of the small ketches moored nearby.

The fight wasn't quite out of her yet.

'If the villas above St Ives can make a living from their position, why shouldn't we,' she told herself, clattering down the steps towards the kitchens.

Chapter Nine

'I don't have any choice,' said Aunt Sara, a few days later, as Jess served up the evening meal in the harbourmaster's cottage. 'I'm sorry, Tom. I've no wish to abandon the harbour, but if I stay, my business will go under before Christmas, unless a miracle happens. And I'm not about to live my life according to miracles. I've had everything I've built up over years taken away from me once before. I'm not letting the likes of Tobias Howells do it again.'

'Does that mean you've found a place?' said Dad.

'I'm signing the lease tomorrow. It's only in St Ives. I won't be far away.'

'And what about you, Jess?'

Jess prodded the potatoes in her soup. 'It isn't so far, Dad.'

'We're not abandoning you, Tom. I'll arrange for one of Pengelly's daughters to pop in and help you when Jess and I aren't here. We might not both be able to get back to you every night, but there are rooms in the building where we can stay.' She brightened. 'If things continue as they are, I'll be able to afford a motorised van by next year, then it will only be a few minutes from here to St Ives, in which case it won't be long until we are back living here with you again.'

'I don't want to leave,' said Jess, hating to see the sadness in his face. 'But Aunt Sara has worked so hard to keep her business going during the war, and now she has a chance to build it into something really profitable. Besides...' She hesitated. For all his kindness, Dad was a proud man and she didn't want to hurt his feelings. But it had to be said. 'It will mean we can still make a living, even if the Bellamys can no longer pay a harbourmaster.'

'That's true enough.' He sat back, cup of tea in hand. 'You're right, sweetheart, and I'd be a selfish old man to insist you stayed to play nursemaid. I'll miss you.'

Jess went over and placed her arms around him. 'I'll miss you too. I'll be back several nights a week, as often as I can until we sort something out.'

'Yes, of course,' he replied, with a smile. 'Don't worry about me, I can manage here.'

'It won't be for long.' Guilt shot through her. The truth was, she'd jumped at Aunt Sara's suggestion. There were so many artists and craftsmen and women in St Ives, there had to be at least a female silversmith. St Ives would give her more of a chance of finding somewhere to learn more skills and begin to work with metals and enamel again.

Already she was saving every penny she could, and Aunt Sara had promised better pay and fewer long hours for her and Morwenna as the business grew. At least if she was improving her metalworking skills, and having the chance to work on her designs, she could eventually set up her own business, however long that took.

Fred Williams, along with several of the other fishermen, had cleaned up and painted some of the boats lying idle, and they were doing a good trade ferrying walkers and artists out into the bay, and to and from St Ives. It meant more customers for the bakery and the little row of surviving shops which, given half a chance, might attract more enterprises to set up over time. But, for now at least, it wasn't enough to keep the harbour going. She couldn't just stay and hope.

*

Having secured her new workroom, Aunt Sara moved quickly. Within weeks, Jess was helping her pack up the little sewing room on the harbour; transferring its contents by means of Tam Jeffries' wagon, pulled by a sturdy little pony, and Tam's grandson, who was glad to earn a few shillings helping them to carry the treadle sewing machine and the bolts of material up the steep steps to the long attic room that had once been used for storing nets. Many such rooms were now being turned into more profitable workspaces to house the influx of painters, along with potters and other artisans.

On the last morning, as she waited for Tam to arrive, with bundles of bedding and clothing at her feet, while Aunt Sara made yet another final check that nothing vital had been overlooked, Jess was joined by Mrs Wilkes.

'So, you'm off then.'

'I'll be back to see Dad in a few days.'

'Don't you worry, I'll keep an eye on him. Katy's a good girl. She'll make sure he doesn't starve.' She smiled a little sadly at Jess. 'You'm doing the right thing, sweetheart. Don't you look back. This place is dying on its feet. You're young. You can't fight the whole world; you need to pick the fights you can win. Your future is what you need to think of now.'

'I still hate the thought of leaving you all.'

'Aye, well. Can't be helped.' Mrs Wilkes scowled towards the road along the headland, where a squat black Bentley was racing from the direction of St Ives, sounding its horn impatiently as it caught up with Tam's more sedate progress. A further sounding of the horn and the vehicle swept round the wagon, roaring up towards Enys Hall. 'Arrogant young sod. Thinks he owns the world. Or at least that he ought to.'

'I hate the thought of so many of the businesses going.'

'Bowing to the inevitable, I'm afraid. There's a few hanging on. But that won't last. You and your aunt are doing the right thing. We might be joining you before long.'

Tam's wagon pulled to its slightly rickety halt next to them. 'Bloody young idiot,' he muttered. 'Showing off like that. I don't care who he thinks he is, he half scared the life out of poor Blossom here, and that ain't right.'

Jess hugged Mrs Wilkes and helped Aunt Sara swing the remaining bundles onto the back of the wagon, before pulling herself up among the pillows and blankets and the last boxes of lace and buttons. They set off slowly up the hill, with Blossom taking the strain in her usual patient manner, urged on by Tam.

As they passed the gateway to Enys Hall, the Bentley emerged at speed, this time with Louisa in the passenger seat.

'Leaving then, I see, Mrs Catchpole,' remarked Tobias, slowing down to keep alongside them. 'The harbour will miss your quaint little shop.'

'Regretfully, one has to expand,' returned Aunt Sara, for all the world as if she were heading for a grand emporium, one too magnificent for the harbour to hold.

'The ladies do insist on having their frills and furbelows; I expect you will find some customers.'

'I'm sure I will. Good morning, Mrs Howells.' Louisa nodded her head in gracious acknowledgement and turned her head away, as if admiring the countryside, far too grand to converse with her tenants. They might as well be doing a midnight flit, thought Jess with irritation.

'Always was a dead-end place, the harbour,' remarked Tobias. 'Old Mr Bellamy let it go to rack and ruin. It always did need a firm hand to make sure it was successful.' His smile had become a positive smirk. 'You're wise running away. I expect I should wish you good luck, Mrs Catchpole.' The motor car swerved round them as the road began to narrow, heading off into the distance, leaving the wagon to make its slow way behind.

'Always did like having power over things weaker than himself, that one,' said Aunt Sara. 'I remember when he was a boy, he was just the kind to enjoy tearing the wings off flies just to watch them struggle. Always had to win to puff himself up, and careful not to pick a fight with anyone his own size. At least if Peter Howells had survived he might have played fair. If his father is letting that young idiot have more influence over the harbour, I'm glad I'm not a part of it.'

The wagon trundled on, creaking and bumping over potholes. As they reached the row of villas next to the town, Jess could make out the Bentley parked in the driveway of the largest house, with Tobias handing Louisa down from the passenger seat before leading her inside.

For the first few weeks in St Ives, Jess was too exhausted to do anything at the end of the day but fall into bed. Aunt Sara was much the same. There was so much to do, organising the new workroom and making sure they fulfilled the new orders that were coming in.

But as things settled down, they finally caught up with themselves. Aunt Sara spent more time drawing up new designs, guided by the illustrations of the newest styles in all the ladies' magazines. She was still hoping to expand and persuade Morwenna to join them full time. For the moment she was still doing her embroidery work at home, where she could help her mother and do her best to improve Ben's spirits, joining them in St Ives only to collect and return her work, staying overnight when they were particularly busy.

Gradually, Jess found she had more energy in the evenings. She enjoyed the novelty of being out on her own and being able to do as she pleased, although she still hoarded as much as she could of her earnings.

Whenever she could, she explored the maze of streets near the front, which had once been crowded with fishermen and nets, but was now inhabited by artists, or being turned into guesthouses for visitors. The only metal workshops she came across seemed to be clearly masculine spaces. Surely there had to be at least one woman somewhere in St Ives, however long it took to find her.

One evening as she was making her way along Porthmeor Beach, she heard her name being called. She turned to find a dark-haired young man about her own age, accompanied by a girl of eight or nine clutching a folder under one arm, making their way across the sands towards her.

'Jessica. It is you. Charlotte said it must be.' Frank's face, like his body, had filled out from its half-starved state, but she would still recognise him anywhere.

'Frank! I heard you had settled here in St Ives.'

'Yes, we are happy here.' He nodded. 'And you, you are visiting?'

'I work here now, with my aunt. She's just set up a dress-making workshop near the front.'

'That is good.' He smiled at Charlotte, who was tugging insistently at his sleeve. 'My sister is asking if you would like to come with us. I'm sure Jessica has plenty of things to do, *chérie*.'

'I've finished worked for the day – I'd love to,' said Jess.

Charlotte made a motion with her right hand.

'We are going to her drawing class.'

'Drawing class?'

Charlotte whispered something in his ear. 'I'm not sure. It's up to Jessica.' He coloured slightly. 'Charlotte is asking if you would be her model. It's a life-drawing class. Very respectable,' he added hastily. 'Women only. I only take her there and I fetch her back. I am not allowed beyond the door and the models are ...' His colour deepened. 'Always with all clothes.'

Jess laughed; it felt like the first time in months, in years, even. 'Well, in that case, I'd love to.'

Charlotte beamed and fell in beside her, taking a quick glance every now and again, as if shy of being caught watching. They led her to a tall, rather shabby building overlooking the sea. At the door Frank stopped. 'You are quite sure, Jessica?'

Charlotte nodded and waved him away, miming drinking from a glass.

He smiled. 'Don't tell them I'm heading to a public house, they'll get the wrong idea.'

Charlotte grinned with an unexpected flash of mischief and grabbed Jess' hand, leading them upstairs.

The top room was a space with tall windows letting in the light and with a view over the sea. They were greeted by a middle-aged woman who introduced herself as Mrs Harris.

'We always welcome new recruits.'

'I'm not an artist,' explained Jess hastily, 'I'm a friend of Charlotte's, I've volunteered to be her model.'

'Then you are very welcome.'

For the next hour or so, Jess sat as still as she could while the women peered at their canvases, working away. She'd thought it would be simple, but before long every bone in her body ached from holding the same position, while the urge to sneeze occurred with alarming regularity.

All the same, she enjoyed the atmosphere of intense concentration; it brought back the atmosphere of the workshop, of being so intent on creating the vision in her mind that nothing else could intrude.

A few of the women were, from the quality of their clothing, the wives and daughters of wealthy men, but others had worn boots and a few even wore skirts that were patched in several places. One or two looked pale with exhaustion, as if they had rushed to the class after a day's hard work.

Jess itched to retrieve her own notebook and pencil, to catch the silhouette of the young woman, auburn hair caught in a Pre-Raphaelite halo in the sun, whose strokes were bold on the page in a way Jess had never seen before. As the pencils scratched, interspersed by the low voice of Mrs Harris making a suggestion here, a sound of encouragement there, she could feel her senses tingling.

This was different to trying to work on her own, making her designs and attempting to keep her dream alive, Jess recognised wistfully. She could feel the creative passion all around her, shared even in silence. It was the kind of silence that used to permeate the workshop when Ben was there, working alongside her. She missed it more than ever.

By the time the lesson was over, she was as stiff as could be, stretching gratefully to get the blood flowing again. As the class broke up in a ripple of conversation, Jess took a quick glance at Charlotte's pencil sketches.

'Why, that really does look like me,' she exclaimed, astonished by the sight of her own face, glimpsed only in the tarnished mirror over the fireplace at home, staring out in concentrated absorption into the distance. The detail was so fine, the shading so rounded, it felt as if it could leap out of the page.

Mrs Harris smiled with unmistakable pride. 'Charlotte has a real gift. We all thought she was far too young to join us when her brother approached us last summer, but she most certainly is not.'

Jess found Charlotte patting her hand. She held out the

most finished sketch. 'It's for you,' said Mrs Harris as Jess hesitated.

'Are you sure?'

Charlotte nodded vigorously.

'Thank you.' She rolled it up carefully to avoid any creasing, placing it deep in her pocket for safety. 'I'll treasure it. And I'll come back and see you, and model for you again, if I may?' Charlotte nodded. 'If that's all right with you, Mrs Harris?'

'Of course,' said Mrs Harris, accompanying them to the door. 'We've few enough volunteers and none of my artists wants to take time from sketching. You'll be most welcome.' As Charlotte raced down the stairs in front of them, she sighed. 'Poor little thing. Heaven knows what they went through during the war before they ended up here. She's lucky to have a brother working all hours to keep a roof over their heads and to afford her lessons. With a talent like hers, we'd take her without payment, but he insists. I think he still can't bear to be beholden to anybody. I'm afraid even after all this time he still worries they will be viewed as a burden.'

'I'm sure they are not.'

'Indeed not. Frank makes frames for many of my ladies' pictures; that helps them out. It can't be easy for him, being father and mother to her as well as the breadwinner. She seems to understand English as well as her brother, but she never speaks. And I have to confess one or two of her early pictures were more than a little disturbing. That's when we decided she would be best joining the ladies here, working on portraits and life drawings for now. Her grasp of detail is extraordinary. She will make a fine illustrator one day.'

'I'm sure she will,' said Jess, as they reached Charlotte waiting for them at the bottom of the stairs. She gave the hand slipped into hers a reassuring squeeze as they made their way out into the evening light.

Charlotte knew exactly where to go, but rather than the nearest public house, she took them to a bench overlooking the sea, where Frank was sitting, deeply absorbed in carving a small piece of wood.

'Good?' he enquired, looking up from the figure of a seal lying sideways on rocks, carved in the same exquisite detail as Charlotte's drawings.

'It was fascinating,' she exclaimed. 'Charlotte is wonderfully talented. I couldn't do anything like that.'

Charlotte tugged at the chain around her neck, pulling out a small silver locket. It opened to reveal a tiny painting of a young woman smiling out into the world, faced on the other side with a young man with Frank's dark hair and thick eyebrows.

'Is that your mother?'

Charlotte nodded, face instantly closing in on itself.

'It's all we have left,' said Frank, taking his sister's hand. 'Even at the worst, we never sold it.'

'I'm so sorry.' His face was as closed as his sister's. Jess swallowed. She couldn't bear to think what had happened to the man and woman in the locket, looking out so eagerly on a world in which they must have had so many hopes and dreams.

'It is the past,' said Frank. 'We are not the only ones, and we must look forward now. Make the best we can.' He grimaced. 'Already the war is being forgotten. I work with boys who are too young, who do not understand what it was like. But for us, it will never vanish.' He shook himself as Charlotte tugged at his hand. 'She is asking...'

'If I'll go again next week? I'd love to.'

Charlotte beamed.

'Thank you. I don't want us to take up all your spare time.'

'To be honest, I don't know many people here. It's nice to see friendly faces.'

His face brightened. 'Then we will show you. Everything there is to see in St Ives. You will soon make friends.'

Charlotte had taken the little wooden seal from his hands, and was holding it up for Jess to admire.

'It's beautiful. It looks just as they do when they come out and sunbathe,' she said with a smile.

'Visitors like them, as a souvenir. A reminder. And you? You said you are working for your aunt – you are doing your enamel work as well?'

Jess shook her head. 'It's not possible to work in the workshop in the harbour any more. I was hoping to find somewhere here. Evening classes, maybe.'

He raised his eyebrows. 'You are looking for a teacher?'

'It seems the only practical solution, for now. I don't want to lose the skills I've already got. At least if I was taking a class I would still be learning, until I'm able to save enough to start up on my own.'

'I see.' He was looking thoughtful. Charlotte, who had been watching them during this conversation, eyes travelling from one to the other, gave him a less than subtle nudge.

Jess's heart missed a beat. 'Do you know of somewhere?'

'Maybe. I put up shelves for a silversmith a few months ago. She was just setting up, but she said something about running classes.'

'That's exactly the sort of thing I'm looking for.'

'Then I will show you? Maybe tomorrow,' he added quickly. 'I think it is too late tonight.'

Jess nodded. 'I would like that. I can meet you here to-morrow evening, if you like.'

'Good. Then we will show you.'

'Thank you.' She met his smile. It was warm, with a touch of shyness. So he hadn't forgotten that moment in the workshop, the night he and Charlotte were rescued. His eyes under the thick brows seemed darker than ever. Their expression had eased a little over the four years that had passed, but she could still glimpse the haunted look in their depths.

'I'm glad we met again,' she said, as they turned to make their way back towards St Ives.

'And I am too,' he replied, gravely. 'Charlotte and I, we have never forgotten the kindness that rescued us from the sea and gave us life.'

At his side, Charlotte slipped her free hand into his, holding on tight as they made their way between the evening strollers on the beach, past the lady painter dabbing away furiously to catch the ever-changing reds and purples of the setting sun; back towards the quiet bustle of the town.

Chapter Ten

'Tobias is offering to help us,' announced Mrs Bellamy at dinner one evening.

Rachel looked up from buttering a slice of Cook's delicious bread. 'Is he? How?'

'He understands these things,' said Louisa, finishing her soup with the polite disinterest of a woman guarding her figure.

Rachel's nerves grated. All those months in France her body had been on the edge of hunger. All those children she had seen with swollen bellies of true starvation, all the mothers struggling to keep them alive in a landscape stripped of every form of sustenance by warring armies. They should be seizing every morsel of food, savouring every last flavour.

She suppressed her urge to say something. Louisa, who had already been nagged by Mama for leaving food when Cook was struggling to do the best with the least ingredients, would only be hurt and their mother would retire with one of her headaches, leaving the rest of them tiptoeing around in the reproachful silence.

'You mean business?' she asked.

'Of course. So much could be done with the harbour. It has so much unfulfilled potential.'

'I'm sure it does.'

'Tobias says it's possible,' said Louisa. 'He understands these things.'

'And we don't?'

'You know nothing about business!'

'We've all heard Papa and the boys talking. I'd say we know as much as anyone. Especially you, Mama. You always helped Papa with the accounts and dealt with the invoices and the payments.'

'My dear, that's hardly running a business.'

'It may not be the visible part, but it's the real heart of things. I'd lay any bet you like that you know more about the harbour than all the Howells put together.'

'Why are you so against them?' frowned Louisa. 'Tobias is volunteering his time to make sure we can stay in this house and our future is secure. It's just your pride that makes you want to throw it all away. And that he talked to me first, not you.'

'Louisa!' exclaimed Mama, warningly, as Hannah came in to clear away the soup bowls and bring in the rabbit pie Cook had prepared. 'Darling, I'm sure Rachel means well, and all we have now is each other.'

Rachel glanced towards her mother. The lines on her face had deepened even further over the past months. Rachel's heart went out to her. When she had been a girl, it had grated that her mother seemed content to run the household and keep the business going without any credit, deferring always to Papa's opinions on most things; even if she might grumble about them once he had gone. Rachel had always promised herself that she would only ever marry a man who treated her as a rational creature and respected her as his equal. The thought of spending her life deferring to anybody made her feel more than a little nauseous.

With older eyes, she had more understanding. At least it was now a little more respectable for a woman to undertake paid employment. When Mama was young, the only choices had been marriage, or living as a governess at the edges of a wealthy household, liable to be dismissed at any minute and with an uncertain future. Mama had never been the bossy kind of woman who ran a charity or a charitable hospital with the force of will Rachel had seen in the women running the field hospitals out in France.

Mama, for all her quickness with numbers, had never had that self-confidence. She'd relied on Papa's approval before accepting she was right. Poor Mama. She had thrown all her hopes, her whole life, into Papa and the boys. She had been living in a daze ever since that first telegram informing them that Oliver was missing, which was followed by weeks of agonising uncertainty until the worst had been confirmed. No wonder the future terrified her. It made Rachel even more determined that they should support themselves.

'Leviathan has been losing money because its time is over,' she said gently. 'If the harbour is to survive, we need to find another way.'

'I suppose what you want is for me to use all my legacy from Peter to support you,' said Louisa. 'Or ask Mr Howells for money. Or maybe you just want me to beg to return to live with them.'

'No, of course not, my darling,' said Mrs Bellamy. 'Not unless you want to, that is. You have your own future to think of. Rachel and I will manage.'

'I don't want to just manage, Mama,' said Rachel. 'Plenty of women are running businesses these days. We had to during the war, and now there are so few men, more women are having to support themselves. I've friends who are working in London as clerks, they're paid so little, far less than the men, they can barely make ends meet, but at least they keep their independence.'

'I don't want to be a clerk,' exclaimed Louisa.

'Maybe we should take Tobias's advice,' said Mrs Bellamy uncertainly.

'It isn't just us,' replied Rachel. 'What's to happen to the harbour? Most of the families there have lived there for generations and most of them have spent their lives working for Leviathan. We can't just abandon them.'

Louisa's face eased into triumph. 'Tobias says the families will be secure and he'll make sure they find work.'

He was lying. Rachel could feel it in her bones. Because they were merely women, he took the three of them for fools he could twist round his little finger.

Her mother was inspecting the pattern of her teacup, while Louisa was avoiding her eye. They all knew it, Rachel thought, however deep the knowledge might be buried. It felt as if the air had been sucked from the room.

The three of them fell silent again as Hannah came to take away the plates, bringing a small syllabub by way of dessert.

As soon as she could, Rachel excused herself, grabbing her coat, and hurried out onto the cliffs, pacing against the wind. During her time driving the ambulance in France, she had grown accustomed to spending every hour of the day pushing her body to its limits, snatching any food available to sustain herself as best she could, sleeping a few hours at a time when she could, always braced for the next explosion that told of a battle beginning, or the nearby crash of mortars that meant the fighting might overtake the makeshift hospital at any minute. However exhausted, she had been instantly awake to take the wounded men in their care to the next deserted farmhouse or abandoned chateau whose cellars might offer them some shelter.

She never would have thought that she might crave that closeness she had felt with the nurses and the stretcher-bearers, all of them living each moment on their nerves, knowing it might be their last. For the first time in her life, she had found a sense of purpose. Then, she had craved a few hours, a few minutes even, of quiet and security to rest and sleep. She had dreamed of Cook's steamed suet puddings with a passion she had never thought she'd had within her. But now she had peace and quiet, she found it unbearable.

She didn't know how far she had walked the wildness of the cliffs, but she couldn't walk for ever. As evening began to turn towards dusk, she wearily made her way back toward Enys Hall.

Down below, tucked within its rocky bay, the harbour was settling in for the night. In the early autumn light, she could see children being shooed home from play, smoke from cooking fires spiralling upward in the still air. The remaining boats rocked gently, seagulls squabbling over scraps on the quayside.

The cottages in the harbour were bound together by the grief of men lost at sea, children left fatherless and mothers struggling to keep a roof over their heads. Of living close to the edges of existence. Everything she had seen had brought its existence into sharp focus.

Even in peacetime, the harbour was the only security any of them had. Without it, it was a frightening, uncaring world out there. She had seen that world, feeling helpless in its overwhelming horror as hell broke lose all around her. The only hope had been the communities surviving, making the best life they could among the mortars of a fight that they had never asked for, waiting for some kind of peace to return again, living for hope, and for their children's future.

The Howellses would never keep the harbour as it was. She had seen the look of scorn on Tobias's face whenever he passed through. He saw the inhabitants as nothing, of no account, because they weren't rich. As if an accident of birth was a moral failure. He would never see the community of the harbour as rich in its own way. He would only see that they were unable to declaim Shakespearian sonnets or pass a suitable comment on a work of art. The outward trappings of civilisation that did not care whose dreams were trodden on because in his world, such people barely counted as civilised in any way.

Enys Hall was far too big and cumbersome for just the three of them – it was calling out to be filled with life again. Surely as a guesthouse, some of that life would be brought back. When she had been little, the workshops on the quay had still provided most things the house had needed, from boots to winter coats, to lamps and candlesticks to the candles themselves.

If there were guests at Enys Hall, ones with money to spend, surely the harbour, with its emerging artists and craft workers, might have a chance to thrive in a new way.

'Good evening, Miss Bellamy.' Lost in thought, she had failed to notice she was no longer alone.

'Ben!' She steadied the colour rising to her cheeks. Her heart thumped painfully in her chest. 'I've never seen you up here before.'

'What you mean to say is that I'm trespassing.'

'No, of course not. That's not what I meant. You know me better than that.'

'Yes, miss.' His voice was dry.

'I'm glad to see you are regaining your strength. I was sorry to hear about your hand. They seemed so optimistic at the hospital.'

'There are worse things can happen to a man, as we both know all too well.'

She glanced at him. But not for you, she thought. To know you will never again be able to do something you love and which gives you a living. Guilt went through her as it had done over and over again since that terrible day, when she had insisted they take the ambulance out one more time, despite the mortars of the approaching battle falling increasingly close to the field hospital. It had been her pride that had dragged her and Ben into the path of the explosion that had destroyed the ambulance, leaving her untouched, but changing Ben's life for ever. If only…

'If you need any assistance…' The pride in his face silenced her.

'I'd best be getting home,' he said stiffly.

'Yes. Yes of course. Ben…'

'Yes, Miss Bellamy?'

'I didn't mean to stop you from coming up here. I know you need to continue to regain your strength. Please don't stop on my account.'

'No indeed, miss.'

Was it her imagination, or was there reproach in his gaze? Whatever it was, heat overcame the chill from the wind on her face.

'Goodnight, then.'

'Goodnight, Miss Bellamy.'

A shot ran out, clear and sharp in the night air. Despite herself, Rachel started violently, instinct sending her towards the ground, only just stopping herself in time.

Ben caught her arm as she stumbled. 'Poachers.'

'Yes, I know. I can't help myself.'

'Me neither,' he replied. 'Bugger, ain't it?'

She returned his smile, for a moment back in the world of mud and broken bodies, where social station, and most of the time even sex, made no difference. The world of the edge of life, where just living each moment was all that mattered.

'I suppose it will ease, in the end.'

'I should damn well hope so. It's embarrassing, trying to throw yourself under the table in the Mermaid for no reason. Not that I've taken to drink, like some of them, you understand.'

'I didn't think it for a minute. I know you far too well.'

'So you do,' he said, voice gentle. 'You always will, Rachel. I wouldn't have it any other way.'

He was so near she could feel his breath warm on her face. Rachel drew in the familiar scent of him, his closeness. Every nerve of her body responded instinctively to his touch, softening the frozen core of her with the memory of the glide of his hands over her bare flesh, the movement of him inside her, the world far away. How simpler life was when there was no tomorrow.

Ben had glanced instinctively towards the light in the drawing room of Enys Hall, where the curtains had not yet been drawn.

'There you go, miss,' he said, returning to formality and quickly releasing her, stepping back so that his gesture of assistance at her near-fall could not be misconstrued by any watching.

'Thank you,' she replied, heart twisting at this loss of intimacy. 'Ben ...'

But he had gone, already striding his way down towards the harbour, shoulders rigid with that damned pride of his, as if he had the devil at his heels.

Blinking away any telltale tears, she turned back to Enys Hall, towards the shadow silhouetted at the window. Mama could think what she liked, Rachel told herself, stuffing her hands in her pockets in the most unladylike manner.

Not that it mattered now. It never would. It never could. Not ever again.

Chapter Eleven

Frank was as good as his word. The next evening, he and Charlotte were waiting on Porthmeor Beach when Jess escaped Aunt Sara's sewing room. Frank led the way through a maze of little alleyways in the Downlong area of the town to a small flight of stairs leading up to what had once been a fisherman's loft.

'We will wait,' he said, as Jess hesitated. 'Or you will never find your way out again. I had to have someone show me the way the first time I came here, too.'

'Thank you. This should only take a few minutes.'

The door at the top of the stairs was slightly ajar, revealing a glimpse of a long room, lit by large windows. Straight in front of her, unmissable from the door, a wooden stand had been set, displaying rows of delicate silver earrings, each one wrought into sinuous shapes that required no other ornamentation.

'Come in!' The woman bent over a long bench at the far end glanced up from her work as Jess knocked.

'Miss Catterell?'

'That's me. It is something particular you are looking for?'

'Oh, I don't want to buy.' Jess blushed furiously at this less than tactful beginning. 'I mean, what you do is beautiful, but I came to enquire about evening classes.'

'I see.'

She hadn't expected Miss Catterell to be so young, not

much older than herself; nor so beautiful, tall and elegant, with the palest skin she had ever seen and a mass of red hair, caught behind her neck with a silk scarf decorated with irises. With her loosely flowing dress, covered by a voluminous apron, she could have stepped out of the Pre-Raphaelite painting Aunt Sara kept, in reproduction form, on her bedroom wall: her only reminder of the elegant surroundings of her married life.

'The classes are for beginners,' said Miss Catterell. 'Women who wish to take up a craft as a hobby.'

'Oh,' said Jess. Rich women, was what she meant. The women from the villas on the cliffs outside the town, carefully set away from any suggestion of fish. The kind of woman Jess was so obviously not, and would never be. Well, that was better than nothing, even if they did spend their time looking down their noses at her.

'I would like to join. I can pay.'

'The current class is halfway through the course. It wouldn't be fair to take a beginner at this point. I've a new series beginning in a few months' time, if you are still interested.'

'I'm not a beginner. I've done metalwork before. And I'd prefer to start straight away, if I can.'

'Silverwork?'

'A little. Mostly copper and pewter. And other metals. I worked as a blacksmith during the war. But it's enamel that's really my passion.'

'A blacksmith?' Miss Catterell put down the fine hammer she had been using and considered Jess thoughtfully. 'So you are familiar with the ways metals work.'

'Yes. When I was working as a blacksmith I loved how it became fluid, like liquid, when it reached a high enough temperature, and then set into something so solid and durable.'

'I see.' Miss Catterell was even more thoughtful. 'Very well. Reach down one of the aprons from the hooks over there and show me what you can do.'

Jess took a deep breath, heart racing. She had an urge to take to her heels before Miss Catterell found out she was bluffing and that she had no skill at all. Steadying her nerves, she pulled the enveloping apron around her and joined Miss Catterell at her bench.

The tools she was given were small and fine. They rested easily in her hands as she was directed towards a small metal bowl Miss Catterell reached down from a shelf.

'It's a trial one. Let's see what you can do.'

Jess took the bowl and placed it firmly on the bench, balancing her hammer in her hand. The first time she had taken up such a hammer, Ben had been at her side, encouraging her, showing her what to do. She could feel him next to her, his face concentrated on seeing how to help, his warmth, the long fingers that could make metal become anything he chose with such dextrous ease. The bowl wavered and jumped around in front of her.

'I'm sorry.'

'That's all right, take your time.'

Jess blinked hard, doubt shooting through her again. What had she been she thinking of? She was the ungainly daughter of a local harbourmaster, who had worked as a blacksmith during the war and played at being a true craftswoman in the workshop behind the forge. How could she ever match up to a woman who had no doubt trained for years, and could make something as delicate as the earrings next to the door?

Jess pulled herself together, remembering the bride's silver hair clasp, with its unique design and intricate mechanism, which had caused such pleasure. The first strikes were clumsy, but gradually she gained a feel for the unfamiliar hammer and found her rhythm. She shut out the woman watching her. She shut out her doubts, everything, until it was just her sensing the metal, persuading it to bend to her will. Slowly, the flat form began to take shape. When she stopped to brush the sweat from her eyes, she found Miss Catterell watching her intently.

'Not bad.'

'It's clumsy. That side is far too uneven.'

'So I see. But I also observed that you have a good eye and you know your material, and you were aware of your own errors. I suspect you might be a perfectionist. You said you worked during the day?'

'As a seamstress. I work for my aunt. We have rooms above the shop. It's only a few streets away. I can afford to pay for lessons.'

'I need to make this business work.'

'Miss?'

'My family never approved. Especially once they realised it wasn't just a whim and it was how I wanted to spend my life and that it's more important to me than a husband and a family. I lost my fiancé in the war, you see. You can't just replace your soul mate because marriage is how your family believe your life should be. My father is stopping my allowance from the end of this month. He thinks that it will bring me to heel and make me agree to marry any man they have in mind.' She sighed. 'After what you have shown me just now, Miss Morgan, I'm not sure I can teach you anything in my beginners' classes; and none of my pupils has so far wished to move onto a higher level of skill. I can't afford to pay an assistant, but I can offer you training if you agree to work for me in your spare time.'

'Yes,' said Jess, before she had time to think this over and be sensible. 'I mean, to being your assistant. If you will train me.'

'But no promises. This may be only for a few weeks. If I can't find more outlets soon, I won't be able to carry on.' She gave a wry smile. 'In which case I might be begging you to teach me how to become a seamstress, to escape being dragged back to a life of leisured boredom, interspersed with charitable works, as I slowly go out of my mind.'

'I'd teach you,' said Jess, not sure if she was serious or not. 'Although I'm sure it won't come to that.' She found Miss Catterell scrutinising her again in a slightly unnerving fashion.

'Good. I'm Diana, by the way. I don't hold with the formalities.'

'Jessica. Jess.'

'Pleased to meet you, Jess. I'm glad you found me. I have a feeling we're going to work well together.'

Jess made her way back down to the street in a daze.

'That's good, isn't it?' said Frank, as they turned to retrace their steps to the beach. 'You will learn more as an assistant than if you were in a class.'

'I don't know what my aunt is going to say.'

'You are learning. Does she need to know more than you have found an evening class?'

'I suppose not,' she replied slowly. 'Not until I'm ready. I might not be doing enamelling, but at least my hands won't forget the metalwork. I sold some of my work during the war; I know I can make things that people like. And I know I could make a much better version of the headband, so it could come apart far more easily.' At his puzzled look, she pulled out her notebook, sketching the design of the bees and the way the headband could be both fitted together and divided.

'That must take skill,' he said, with a smile, turning to explain the details in French to his sister, who was peering at the drawing, head on one side, trying to puzzle out the workings of the mechanism. 'Charlotte,' he reproved gently, as she began to riffle through the rest of the notebook.

'It's all right, I don't mind,' said Jess. 'I've seen your beautiful drawings, Charlotte. Mine are just plans for designs.' She had never shown anyone her ideas before. It felt strange seeing Charlotte turning the page, examining her little sketches one by one. As she reached the one of the rays of sun caught behind the sailing boat, she exclaimed something.

'Charlotte is right,' said Frank. 'That one is very Art Deco.'

'Art Deco?'

'It's a new style, it's become even more popular since the war. Art Nouveau is still popular with some, but Art Deco is becoming all the rage. At least that's what the artists here tell me.' He grinned. 'They tend to be very particular about the framing, that it should reflect the elegance of the lines.'

'Oh,' said Jess. 'I don't know anything much about styles, I'm afraid. Ben told me a little about Art Nouveau, but I didn't think much about it being fashion. I just did what pleased me and what I thought would work best in metal and enamel. I can see I need to know more if I'm to try and sell my work – I can't just please myself.'

'If you like …' Frank hesitated.

'Yes?'

'I am making so many frames, for an exhibition. The artists I work for, they use many styles, but one of the painters is very fond of Art Deco. If you would like to see his work, I can show you.'

'I would love to,' said Jess eagerly. 'I want to learn

everything I can. I've been so shut away in the harbour, I don't know anything at all.'

'Except to make beautiful things, your own way,' he replied.

'I suppose.' She met the dark eyes and felt an unexpected blush reaching up from her toes, threatening to envelop every part of her. 'Look,' she said, unfastening the pendant around her neck to hide her confusion, holding it out for Charlotte to see. 'These are the bees. It was a trial piece for the headband. I know it's not perfect, but I wear it all the time to remind me that I want to do so much better.'

'It is beautiful,' said Frank, bending over as Charlotte examined the oval pendant closely, her forefinger tracing the fine lines of metal creating the form for the enamel, curious as to how it was made. 'No one in St Ives makes anything quite like that.'

'The woman I made the final piece for loved it,' said Jess, frustration rushing through her. 'And I was starting to get more commissions. I know I can do it. I just need to be able to set up my own workshop.'

'You will. They are so beautiful I am sure of it.'

'Well, at least I've got a better chance now. Thank you for telling me about Miss Catterell. I was beginning to think I'd never work in metal again.'

'It was your skill that made her take you on as an assistant.'

'But I still might never have found her,' she replied.

'Then I'm glad I remembered her,' he said with a smile, as Charlotte returned the notebook and they made their way back along the beach.

Chapter Twelve

Over the next months, as autumn turned into winter, Jess sewed for Aunt Sara by day, escaping to Miss Catterell's workshop several evenings a week. Under Diana's tuition, her skills rapidly improved. Sometimes, she felt her head was so stuffed full of information it would burst. But however tired she was leaving the sewing room, the short walk along the seafront to meet Frank and Charlotte for their regular walks revived her.

It seemed that Frank made frames and display stands for every artist and craft worker in St Ives, or at least put up shelving and created long tables out of abandoned pieces of wood. He introduced her to all those they met on their evening walks and gave her any information he came across about exhibitions of their work. Jess drank it all in, each new collection setting her mind fizzing with ideas.

Even on the coldest days, when the wind whipped up the waves into great crashing rollers sending plumes of spray against the dark rocks, she found painters sitting on the Island, a grassy peninsula stretching out from the broad curve of Porthmeor Beach, or on the cliffs overlooking the bay; women, as well as men. And not all of them were rich, many struggling to make a living. There was even a woman photographer, with a new lighter form of camera, setting up to capture both the wild winter storms and the everyday life in the harbour. Tucked away in the streets among the fishermen there were potters and sculptors working busily away.

It was so different from the quiet she found whenever she went back home to visit Dad in the harbour below Enys Hall. With so many of the little businesses now closed, and little to seduce the few out-of-season visitors from the varied attractions of St Ives, the quay was ominously silent, with only a few shabby fishing boats left.

Enys Hall appeared equally forlorn. She saw Mrs Bellamy, sometimes with her daughters, wandering in the gardens if the day was sunny, but only briefly. Otherwise it looked shut up, as if the family had gone away.

Then suddenly, as the first signs of spring arrived, there was no time to visit studios in St Ives, or even meet Frank and Charlotte for a few minutes on the beach, as the store on Oxford Street ordered a selection of garments for Aunt Sara to deliver in person.

'Two weeks!' exclaimed Morwenna, excitement turning to alarm as she walked over to join them in poring over the required designs. 'Some of this embroidery is really detailed. They're only giving us two weeks?'

'They are using these as samples of what they want,' said Aunt Sara, triumph mixing with apprehension in her face. 'I've done this kind of thing before for them – it's the way Barringtons always works. They are testing our ability to deliver, as well as our quality, which means they must be seriously considering using us to supply them on a regular basis. They are a touch old-fashioned to my mind, but this could be the making of us. Supplying Barringtons opens doors to all kinds of places; I could even think of approaching Selfridges next year. It's a pity we haven't the time to train up more girls to help us. We'll just have to do this ourselves. You're going to have no time for your evening classes for the next two weeks, Jess – you'd better let them know straight away.'

'Yes, Aunt Sara,' said Jess. She was glad for Aunt Sara, who had worked so hard for this, but she was buzzing with ideas she wanted to work on, and she hated letting down Diana, who had commissions of her own. But it was only for a fortnight, she reminded herself. And if they succeeded, they might never have to worry about finding work again.

For the next two weeks they worked all hours. On the final three nights before Aunt Sara was due to take the garments to London, Morwenna stayed with them in St Ives so they could work uninterrupted to get the job done on time.

On the last day, they barely stopped, taking it in turns to snatch cups of tea and the large fruitcake Morwenna had brought as a good luck present from Mrs Wilkes to help them on. It was after midnight, with her eyes bleary, when Jess finished her final seam. A few minutes later, Morwenna put the last stitches on her embroidery. Aunt Sara carefully pressed the finished garments and hung them up.

'Not bad,' she said, inspecting them carefully, snipping a thread here and there. 'Not bad at all.' Her usually severe face broke into a slow smile. 'I have to confess, they've come out well. They're beautiful. I defy anyone to better them. If we don't get more orders on the back of this, I'll eat my hat. Maybe we should leave them like that until the morning so they don't get creased again. No, on second thoughts, I don't want to risk being late to the train station. We'll pack them up tonight.'

They wrapped the dresses in tissue paper, carefully folding them until they fitted into the suitcase Aunt Sara had brought with her from London, which was battered with much use, but sturdy.

'I think this deserves a toast,' said Aunt Sara, bringing out a dusty bottle of brandy. She poured a generous amount for each of them. Jess coughed as the fiery liquid caught the back of her throat.

Next to her, Morwenna was eyeing her glass as if she had just been invited to drink poison, before politely taking a sip. Her face creased as she swallowed, nearly choking.

'I know why my granddad was a member of the Temperance Society,' she gasped as soon as she could breath again.

Aunt Sara grinned. 'Oh, it's a taste you can get used to. Although maybe I should bring champagne when I return from London.'

'Champagne...' Morwenna's eyes were round.

'I think you deserve a sip of champagne after all our hard work. This really could set us up for life, you know.'

Jess was slowly drifting off in her chair, warmed by the brandy, her body relaxing as the urgency of the last two weeks floated away. She might be utterly exhausted, but she was still itching to join Diana to catch up as much as she could while Aunt Sara was in London, just as she had promised. Although for now, her back and shoulders ached, and her eyes twitched crazily – all she wanted to do was sleep. She wasn't even sure she had the energy to make her way to her own bed.

As if from a distance, she could hear Sara and Morwenna discussing something about designs and fashion houses, their voices becoming drowsier by the minute. She was quiet and she was comfortable and she wasn't going to think about the future, not until tomorrow.

It was the smell of smoke that woke her. She must have been asleep for several minutes at least. The lamp had gone out and the fire had died in the grate, leaving the bitter chill of a February night hanging in the air. Aunt Sara had gone to bed, but Morwenna was still curled up asleep in her chair, almost untouched brandy on the table next to her.

All was quiet and peaceful, with the sound of waves breaking gently on the shore. She must have been imagining things. Jess leant back, eyes closing, drifting back into unconsciousness.

This time there was no mistake. The acrid taste caught at the back of her throat, sending her coughing. She hurried to the window. Light flickered below in the street, coming from the warehouse next door, accompanied by the sounds of shouts of alarm.

As she turned back towards Morwenna, she could make out a faint roll of smoke making its way through the gap beneath the door. From below, there came a deep and ominous crackle.

'Morwenna!' Jess was on her feet in an instant, shaking her companion urgently.

'All right, all right,' Morwenna protested sleepily.

Jess shook her again. 'Get up. You have to get up. We need to get out of here.'

Morwenna coughed as the first trail of smoke snaking its way towards them reached her. She was awake in an instant. 'That's fire.'

'It's next door, but it sounds as if it's spreading downstairs. I'll get Aunt Sara. We need to get to safety.'

Aunt Sara was deeply asleep on her bed, still in her clothes, with the coverlet pulled roughly over her.

'Jess? What is it? Is it morning already?'

'We have to get out, Aunt Sara. There's a fire, and it's coming this way.'

'Fire?' Aunt Sara was on her feet in an instant, trailing the coverlet behind her.

'Can't you smell it?'

'Good grief, yes, and hear it, too.' She began pulling on her boots.

As they reached the main room, they were met by Morwenna closing the door, pushing a coverlet against the gap.

'It's already properly alight down below; it looks like the stairs will go at any minute.'

'Then it'll have to be the window,' said Aunt Sara.

While Morwenna stuffed what materials they could to keep out the smoke for as long as possible, Jess pulled up the sash window overlooking the street. It looked as if half the row was now alight, wind sending great gusts down the alleyways, followed by the dance of firelight. Families were piling out of the cottages on either side of the narrow thoroughfare, babies and small children passed from one to the other, men and women flinging as many belongings as they could retrieve out in the street.

'We can't get down,' she called to the men attempting to break down the sturdy door to the warehouse below. 'The stairs are on fire.'

Jess returned to Morwenna, who was beginning to gasp for air, as the next billow of smoke reached them through the lengths of cotton and linen stuffed beneath the door.

'It'll be all right,' she said. 'They are fetching a ladder.' The heat was growing unbearable, the paint was beginning to peel, while a roar like that of a wild animal was approaching, with a huge crashing of beams below. 'Get as close to the window as you can.'

She pulled Morwenna to her feet, practically dragging her between the spirals of smoke snaking up through the floorboards. It seemed an eternity until they reached Aunt Sara, who was watching out for the promised ladder. In the darkness, the street below was alive with shadows rushing here and there or clustered in groups. Jess could hear shouts of encouragement as a chain of buckets and water swung into action.

'They're on their way,' said Aunt Sara. 'Get next to the window. We might not have much longer.'

'Stay here,' said Jess, placing Morwenna as close as she could to the fresh air. Taking the deepest breath she could and ignoring Aunt Sara's protests, she raced back to where the suitcase was lying on the cutting table, with Aunt Sara's overnight bag placed neatly on top, ready for the morning. She swung the bag over her shoulders, grabbing the handle of the suitcase and stumbled back, lungs exploding, eyes stinging so that she could barely keep them open.

'You little fool!' She'd never been so glad to hear Aunt Sara's scolding. The suitcase was taken from her, and she was pulled forcibly towards the window, where she collapsed, retching. Sea air rushed into her lungs in great gulps. She breathed in deep.

'Don't you ever do that again,' said Aunt Sara, between fits of coughing. 'Nothing is worth losing you.'

'You can't abandon the samples,' retorted Jess, as her breath returned. 'Not after we half killed ourselves finishing them.'

'The ladder's arrived,' called Morwenna, before Sara could reply.

'And about time too.' Sara placed the suitcase next to the window, helping Morwenna to balance the ladder securely against the windowsill. 'Right, you first, Morwenna. Give Jess a chance to catch her breath.'

Morwenna hesitated for only a moment, before hitching up her skirts and swinging herself onto the ladder to shouts of encouragement. A cheer went up as she reached the ground.

'You next, Jess.'

'The fire's nearly through.'

'Then be quick. I need someone with their wits about them to catch the suitcase. I'm not having you risk your life for nothing. Get on with you.'

There was no time to argue. The wood of the door was beginning to crack. It could only be a matter of minutes. Balancing the bag securely on her back, Jess shot down the ladder as fast as she could manage. As she reached the bottom, she shouted, holding out her arms to catch the suitcase, which landed with such force she fell backwards, only saved by the burly fisherman behind, who steadied her.

'Come on!' shrieked the woman next to her, hopping up and down in an agony of suspense. Aunt Sara swung one leg over, then another. The ladder swayed a little. Aunt Sara held on tight. Jess could see her trying to balance herself.

'That thing's goin' to bloody fall,' muttered Jess' rescuer, releasing her to grab the base of the ladder. Above them, the sewing room exploded into a wall of fire.

'Get back, it's going to go!' came a shout. Jess was pulled away from the building, between the raining down of tiles and glass, as flames shot up through the roof and high into the air. From the corner of her eye, she saw the ladder topple sideways, wobble for an agonising moment, then crumple onto the ground.

Chapter Thirteen

Still clutching the precious suitcase, Jess was ushered into one of the cottages further down the street.

'You'll be safe here,' said the elderly woman who had turned her front room into an instant place of refuge for those displaced by the fire. 'They don't think it'll reach this far.' At every corner of the room, mothers were huddled on the floor attempting to still the terrified sobs of small children, with more families arriving every minute, coats and blankets covering their night clothes in an attempt to keep out the bitter cold, having been abruptly forced to leave their homes.

'Jess!' Morwenna emerged from the group. 'Thank goodness. They wouldn't let me back, they said the whole row collapsed.'

'I don't think it's that bad.' She thrust the suitcase into her arms. 'Keep hold of this, I need to find Aunt Sara.'

She shot out again, ducking under the arm of a man shepherding yet more mothers and children away from the danger.

'The woman on the ladder,' she called to passers-by. 'Have you seen her? Is she safe?'

'Jess!' One of the men fighting the flames handed his bucket to a companion and sped towards her. 'Thank goodness you are safe.'

'Frank!' She hugged him tight as his arms came around her. 'Have you seen Aunt Sara?'

He released her. 'No. I have only just got here, a few minutes ago. Charlotte could see the flames from her room. The whole street went up in minutes. I was thinking the worst.'

'We got out, thanks to Aunt Sara. But now I can't find her.'

'She's over there,' called one of the other men. 'It looks bad I'm afraid, love. The doctor's with her.'

Jess left Frank and raced in the direction of a shop that had been turned into a makeshift hospital for firefighters nursing burns, and children coughing from the effects of smoke. In the far corner, the doctor was bending over a figure lying on a makeshift stretcher. She could just make out the distinctive pattern of her skirt.

'Aunt Sara!' Sickness rose in her throat. Not Aunt Sara. Please, not Aunt Sara.

'Where's my suitcase?'

Sara's voice was weak but as forthright as ever. Jess could have wept with relief.

'It's all right, Aunt Sara. Morwenna has it. Don't worry, she's guarding it with her life.'

'She'd bloody better be.' Sara ignored the tutting from the doctor at such disgraceful language from a supposedly respectable female.

'She knows how important it is. Are you hurt?'

'Of course I'm hurt. I wouldn't be here being prodded by this young man if I wasn't.' She sat up. 'I'm perfectly all right. It's just bruising. There's no need to fuss, doctor. I'll live. And I need to get to the train station.'

'I'm afraid you're not going anywhere, madam,' replied the

doctor. 'That arm is broken and it looks as if you may have at least two cracked ribs.'

'Can't you just strap me up?'

The doctor tutted again, more loudly this time. 'My dear lady, I can't possibly do such a thing. It would be most irresponsible. Do you have any idea how lucky you are to be alive?'

'More than most,' returned Sara crossly. She coughed, drawing in her breath sharply, in a gasp of pain.

'See what I mean?'

'I'll go to London,' said Jess. 'If you give me the directions to Barringtons, I'll take your place. I've worked on everything; I can answer any questions they might ask.'

Aunt Sara scowled at the doctor, who was already retreating to his less troublesome patients.

'Jess, I appreciate the gesture, but you've never been to a big town, let alone a huge city like London. Help me up. You can come with me and carry the suitcase. I'm not missing this opportunity.' She attempted to stand, but sat down immediately, cursing under her breath.

'Don't worry,' said Jess. 'I'll find a way. We can't miss this chance.'

'Well, you can't go on your own.'

'I'm sure Morwenna will come with me, if we can find enough for a second ticket.'

Aunt Sara hesitated. 'That's better than an unaccompanied young woman travelling on her own. My ticket is in my bag, use that. There's enough in my purse to get a return ticket for Morwenna as well, and for a cab once you get to Paddington. You'll find a card with the address. All you need to do is to show it to a cab driver and he'll take it there. You need to speak to Mr Simms. No one else. Mr Simms.'

'I'll make sure.'

'And you can't go like that, you'll catch your death.'

Before Jess could open her mouth to protest, there was a minor commotion among the women, resulting in a heavy coat being thrust into her hands, followed by a hat.

'I can't—'

'Yes you can,' said Aunt Sara firmly.

'Don't you worry, Jess, I can borrow mum's coat if needs be,' called a voice from the darkness.

'Thank you,' whispered Jess, eyes filling with tears at such kindness as she hurried back to where Morwenna was waiting with the suitcase, Frank standing next to her.

'Here she is,' said Morwenna.

'Thank goodness.' Frank turned, relief on his face.

'I'm all right. I found Aunt Sara. I hope you don't mind Morwenna, I said we'd go to London in her place.'

'Jess, no,' exclaimed Frank, horrified. 'Not after all this.'

'The two of us will be safe,' said Morwenna, sounding a little shaky, determined. 'I don't want to let down Mrs Catchpole.'

'Not after we've worked so hard to get this commission. Aunt Sara said it could be the making of her business. We've got to at least try.'

'Then I will help you with the suitcase,' said Frank.

They set off towards the railway station, but even that short walk was too much for Morwenna, who was forced to stop several times, overcome with bouts of coughing. They were nearly there when she began to retch, crouching over the gutter as she vomited.

'I'm sorry,' she wailed, as Jess helped her to her feet. 'I'm so sorry. I'll be better now, I promise.'

'It's my fault,' said Jess. 'You breathed in more smoke than me – I shouldn't have forced you to come.'

She could have kicked herself. She had been so determined

to get to London she had pushed aside all other consideration. She had left Aunt Sara to the care of strangers, and now
she had forced Morwenna to practically run through St Ives
in this state, and without even a hat or coat to protect her.

'I'll be better in a few minutes,' whispered Morwenna.

'You need to stay here,' replied Jess. 'You can't possibly go
to London, not like this. I'll take you back to Aunt Sara. She
needs someone to look after her,' she added as Morwenna
began to protest.

'I'll take her,' said Frank, shrugging off his jacket and
placing it around Morwenna's shoulders. 'There will still be
doctors looking after people hurt in the fire. They will know
how to help Morwenna too.'

'Thank you. So that means you've got to go back,
Morwenna.'

Morwenna put her head in her hands, clearly feeling
queasy again.

'Jess…' Frank's face was filled with concern.

'I'll be as safe as houses, don't worry. And I still have my
blacksmith's arm, should I need it.' She caught his smile in
the faint light from the street lamp. 'Please don't stop me.'

'I wouldn't even try.'

'And I'll be back before you know it.'

'I hope.' The warmth of his hand rested briefly against hers
as he handed her the suitcase.

Frank waited until she reached the station, then turned,
helping Morwenna to her feet, supporting her as they made
their way back towards Aunt Sara.

Jess just had time to clean the soot away from her face
and hands and brush down the suitcase as best she could
before the train drew up. She climbed up the steps into the
narrow corridor, making her way along until she found a

compartment occupied by an elderly gentleman fast asleep in one corner alongside a respectable-looking woman in a tweed coat and large hat. The woman looked up only briefly before returning to her perusal of her newspaper.

Jess settled herself down next to the window on the opposite side and checked the contents of the suitcase. To her relief, the dresses all looked unharmed and there appeared to be little hint of smoke. She placed the case carefully in the rack above her head and settled back down, just as, with a jolt and a shudder, the wheels began to turn. The train set off, gathering speed in a cloud of steam.

Jess leant back in her seat. Excitement shot through her, along with sheer terror. Having spent all her life in the tightly-knit confines of the harbour, to her St Ives had seemed adventure enough. She had never imagined travelling as far as Devon, while London might as well have been the moon. She had always been only a few doors away from friendly faces and people she knew would help. Now she would be completely reliant on herself. She took a deep breath, trying to settle her nerves.

'You all right then, are you, dear?' The woman in the hat had put down her newspaper and was eyeing her sympathetically.

'Yes, thank you,' said Jess. 'I've just never been on a train before. It's such a strange sensation.'

The woman smiled. 'Dreadful things. Noisy and smelly, like those motor cars young people have taken to racing about in these days, cluttering up the countryside. But very useful.' She dived into her pocket, pulling out a small tin decorated with an image of a chubby little girl, face surrounded by an impossible amount of golden ringlets. 'I find a humbug generally does the trick.'

'Thank you,' said Jess, taking one of the proffered sweets.

The woman nodded and returned to her reading. The elderly gentleman snorted softly in his sleep. Jess rolled the comforting sweetness in her mouth, relaxing a little. By the time the humbug was finished, she was fast asleep.

Chapter Fourteen

Jess arrived in London dazed by the clatter and stench of Paddington Station.

She emerged into a whirlwind of rush and noise she had never imagined. Horse-drawn carts wrestled for space with more motor cars than she had ever thought existed, all rushing by at impossible speeds with deafening roars of engines and screeching of brakes. Even the pedestrians hurried on their way, as if late for an urgent appointment, looking neither right nor left, intent on their destination.

She hovered for a few minutes at the edge of the crowd, feeling conspicuous at not knowing what she was doing, and observing the more seasoned travellers confidently flagging down a cab, giving instructions to the driver before stepping inside. Holding her suitcase tight, she took a deep breath and followed suit, holding out the business card to the driver, who nodded.

'Barringtons eh, miss? One of the best on Oxford Street, that.'

'So I've been told,' said Jess in relief at the man being familiar with the place at all, negotiating the unfamiliar catch and placing herself and the suitcase inside.

From the moment they set off, she was mesmerised. The streets were full of women as well as men, she noticed with surprise, and not all accompanied. They passed groups of two or three women together, but there were also some who walked alone, with the air of this being perfectly acceptable. At home, Rachel Bellamy was seen as an oddity with her lone walks across the cliffs, but in London a woman striding along the streets attracted little attention.

This was a new world, thought Jess, as the cab wove its way through thoroughfares, to much shouting and cursing from the drivers of the vehicles and the sounding of horns that had her nearly jumping out of her skin. Things had changed in Cornwall after the war, but this was different. It was both alarming and exhilarating. And those women taking their own way through life with all the confidence in the world gave her an instant ambition to join them. Finally, the cab emerged into Oxford Street, depositing her in front of the imposing facade of Barringtons.

Her reception was less than encouraging. Jess found herself being looked up and down with scorn by a male shop assistant. She was horribly aware that, for all her best efforts, the cream of her blouse was smudged with the remains of a sooty stain and her skirt was creased. Even the coat thrust so kindly into her hands was made for warmth rather than elegance, and retained a faint aroma of herring, while the close-fitting cloche hat had seen better days.

Having clearly decided she was not the kind of customer to make the company a fortune, the assistant pointedly attempted to ignore her existence.

'Mr Simms is not available.'

'Yes he is,' she said firmly. 'He's expecting me.'

'He's in a meeting. May I suggest you come back to-morrow.'

'My appointment is with him today,' said Jess. She held out Aunt Sara's card.

'You are Mrs Catchpole?'

'Her representative.' Jess raised her chin. 'My aunt has

been injured. I've come in her place. She has important business here. I've no intention of being late.'

The assistant hesitated, doubt appearing in his face. His expression brightened as a tall young man, who had been in conversation with one of the female sales assistants at a counter stocking cosmetics, made his way towards them, attracted by the commotion. The assistant handed him the card, explaining in a low voice to the newcomer, who nodded and strode purposefully in her direction. Jess braced herself.

'Good morning, miss. I believe you have an appointment with Mr Simms?'

'Yes. I'm delivering the samples from Mrs Catchpole.'

'Yes, of course.' To her relief, the man smiled, the creasing of his skin illuminating the deep scar running down one side of his face, reaching to the side of his mouth. 'You must be Miss Morgan.'

'Yes,' said Jess, in surprise.

'Mr Edwards. I'm Mr Simms' deputy. A Mr Dupont sent a telegram message on behalf of your aunt to alert us to the fact you were coming in her place.'

'Thank goodness.' She could have hugged Frank for his thoughtfulness. At least now she had a chance.

'I'm afraid Mr Simms is in a meeting that is taking longer than expected; he asked me to look after your aunt when she arrived, so you will have to do with me.'

Jess looked at him anxiously. 'You know about the samples that were ordered?'

'I do.' He had startling blue eyes, which were taking in her slightly dishevelled appearance. 'Come up to my office. I think maybe a cup of tea might be in order.'

She followed him into the back of the shop to a maze of offices and workshops. At the end, next to a door bearing a large brass plate declaring *Mr Simms, Manager*, Mr Edwards ushered them inside.

'Miss Fairbairn,' he called. A smartly dressed young woman appeared from an adjoining room, smoothing down her skirt. 'Miss Fairbairn, this is Miss Morgan. She's travelled from Cornwall, I think she might, er...' He cleared his throat.

Miss Fairbairn grinned. 'Follow me, Miss Morgan,' she said, prim as could be. 'I'll show you where you can wash your hands. Men!' she added in a conspiratorial whisper as she led the way down a corridor. 'They are hopeless when it comes to bodily functions. Are you the one who's brought Mrs Catchpole's dresses from Cornwall?'

'Yes.'

'We're so excited to see them. I worked for your aunt when she ran her own fashion business before the war.' She snorted. 'Before that husband of hers drummed up that ridiculous accusation of adultery, so he could replace her for a girl half his age. I'm ashamed to say the little hussy was my assistant.'

'She was?'

'Oh yes.' Miss Fairbairn ushered her into what appeared to be a minor palace of tall mirrors and washbasins, each with their own gleaming tap. 'Scheming little minx. I never thought she had it in her. I mean, she was too lazy to do the work effectively, but you know the kind. Not a bit of sense in their pretty little heads but cunning as a snake and perfectly ruthless. The kind who knows if you flatter some men for long enough they'll fall for it, especially if you are prepared to, well, you know.'

'I'm sure,' said Jess, trying to sound worldly wise, rather than open-mouthed. This was more like a storybook than real life.

Poor Aunt Sara. No wonder she was so very determined to regain her business and escape the gossip and humiliation.

'She got what she wanted all right,' Miss Fairbairn was saying. 'Once she and Mr Catchpole started disappearing into his office for hours on end and he began to blatantly take her out to restaurants and the theatre and didn't care who saw them, well, we all knew the writing was on the wall. I wasn't staying long after some little tart had been promoted over me; and once he decided he was going to marry her, I was out of there like a shot, I can tell you.' She paused. 'I'm sorry about your aunt, though. She was a nice woman. Hard taskmaster, but fair. She had a good head on her shoulders. Of course, I jumped at the chance when she approached me about providing stock for Barringtons. I remember the quality of her work.'

'Aunt Sara is hoping to grow her business again.'

'I've no doubt she'll succeed. She always was the brains, that was obvious. That little schemer soon jumped ship, you know, the moment the business began to fail. Served him right, the old fool.' She lowered her voice. 'In fact, if you ask me, it might be a stroke of luck, Mr Simms still being on the other side of town. Mr Edwards is younger, more open to new ideas. And at least he's prepared to respect a woman's opinion.'

Jess followed Miss Fairbairn back through the corridors. When they reached the office, Mr Edwards had opened the suitcase and removed the first layer of tissue paper.

'Oh my goodness,' breathed Miss Fairbairn. 'That embroidery! It's exquisite. Mrs Catchpole said she'd come across the best embroiderer she'd ever seen.'

'It's not me,' said Jess hastily. 'I don't have the patience. Or the eye. I just do the seams and the hems.'

'But where would the embroidery be without a skilled

seamstress?' Miss Fairbairn lifted each garment out carefully, hanging them up against the wall.

The gowns were a little creased after their journey, but none the worse for wear. There might have been just the faintest hint of smoke, but then the air in London was so foul it could be mistaken as coming simply from their journey through the streets.

'These are beautifully finished,' said Mr Edwards. 'You were quite right, Miss Fairbairn. I apologise if I ever appeared to doubt your judgement.'

'No need. If you did have doubts, you hid it well. But you have to admit, there are skilled workers outside London.'

Mr Edwards laughed, his face relaxing. He must have been a handsome man before the war. Despite the puckering scar to mar the regularity of his features, distorting the edge of one eye, his looks were striking. A sense of profound sadness went through her. Even in her dazed state as she was whirled through the streets, she hadn't missed the sight of beggars, many with limbs missing, at street corners. It wasn't only Ben who had lost so much.

'Miss Fairbairn had to fight her corner against both of us, I'm afraid, Miss Morgan. Mr Simms and I had searched high and low for someone to take on these new styles, but nothing quite worked. I'm glad Miss Fairbairn persuaded us to take a chance on a woman whose firm in London had a reputation for shoddy work.'

'As I told you, only after she left,' returned Miss Fairbairn. A wicked half-smile appeared on her face. 'When I first drove trams during the war, some people – women as well as men – used to refuse to board while there was a woman in charge. But they got used to idea, especially when it was that or stay put at home. Women have been told for far too long

145

we are just there to be handmaidens to our personal lords. You might try to put us back in our box, but it won't work.'

'I never said I wanted to,' replied Mr Edwards. 'I worked alongside plenty of women during the war. It taught me to have nothing but the greatest of respect.'

'You tell Simms that,' muttered Miss Fairbairn as she returned to inspect Morwenna's work. 'I don't suppose we could steal her, the woman who did this?'

'You could try, although I'm not sure Aunt Sara would be prepared to let Morwenna go.'

'I certainly wouldn't, if I was her,' conceded Miss Fairbairn, hurrying towards the door as officious footsteps made their way along the corridor towards them.

Mr Simms was a short, squat little man in his late fifties, who nodded briefly at Jess before turning to peer at the garments hung up for his inspection with a critical air. Jess did her best to answer questions about timing and delivery, thankful that Miss Fairbairn was able to vouch for Aunt Sara's reliability and professional reputation. Jess couldn't help noticing that while Mr Simms might be in charge of the department, he tended to defer to Miss Fairbairn's expertise, without quite saying as much. After a while, her head began to feel like lead.

'Do you have somewhere to stay?' asked Miss Fairbairn, as Mr Simms finally disappeared to keep the rest of the departments up to his exacting standards.

'I need to get back home. They said at the station there was a night train. If you could please help me find a cab, I can easily get back to Paddington in time.'

'Nonsense. We can't send you back straight away. You must be exhausted. You can stay with me. The apartment's very respectable. I'm not allowed gentlemen past the front door. Besides, you haven't had an answer from Mr Simms yet.' A thoughtful look came over her face. 'If he doesn't accept them, I may have some other ideas. I know one or two women who run their own businesses who I'm sure would be interested in work as good as this. Don't worry about your aunt – I can easily arrange for a telegram to reassure her you are quite safe.'

Jess opened her mouth to protest, then shut it again. How could she resist?

Chapter Fifteen

Jess followed Miss Fairbairn to her lodgings a short distance away from Oxford Street, up steep stairs smelling of smoke and cooking, to the apartment shared with three other young women.

The house, which had been divided up to accommodate single women working as clerks or in the nearby department stores, was filled with flats having similar arrangements. Even in the harbour, Jess had never known a dwelling so closely crammed. As they climbed endless flights of rickety stairs, she could hear women's voices on all sides. There was even a small electric cooker consisting of two rings set on the second-floor landing by way of a kitchen.

'We're lucky, we've got our own electric stove,' said Miss Fairbairn, as they passed two girls heating up soup from a can. 'Most of the others have to share this. It's quite an art cooking on one electric ring; we know every cheap restaurant for miles around, believe me. Nearly there. I'm at the top, I'm afraid.'

As they were about to head up the final flight of stairs, the door to one of the flats was flung open, revealing a fair-haired young woman in a silk dressing gown, a brush in one hand, dressing gown flying open revealing bare legs up to her silk camisole. Jess never seen so much female flesh on display in her life. Aunt Sara would probably have dragged her out of there in an instant as a house certain to be of ill repute.

'The bloody sod, you'll never guess what he's done now—' She caught sight of Jess. 'Oh. Hello. I didn't know you had company, Annette.'

'This is Jess, from work. She was stuck for a place to stay, so I said she could have Sylvie's bed for tonight.'

'Damn, and I've got tickets for that new dance hall you were on about. I was going to suggest you came with me. I'm not going on my own.'

'What happened to Harry? You were all over him last week.'

'I'm not going out anywhere with him, not after that last trick. I'm not going to let him walk over me, not for anything. He practically had his tongue down the throat of one of the other girls, when he knew I was watching. You should have seen the look on her face; she's been after him for months. Well, good luck to her. If he thinks that'll make me jump into bed with him, he's got another think coming. That's not love, that's blackmail. He told me straight he wasn't going to use a you-know-what, so what kind of fool does he take me for, risking getting pregnant for his pleasure?' She sniffed defiantly. 'I'm off men for life. Mama was right – they really are only after one thing and most of them ain't fussy. It's not flattering.'

'I'm sorry, Cassie,' said Annette. 'I'm sure you'll find someone else to go with you tonight.'

'I'm only going to fall in love with women from now on,' announced Cassie, as a parting shot. 'At least you can talk to them and they don't all see themselves as the centre of the universe.'

Jess climbed the last of the stairs in a daze. She had a feeling she ought to be swooning away in horror and fleeing into the street from such a hotbed of immorality, and was rather surprised at the thrill coursing through her veins.

The harbour might have its uncertainties, but essentially nothing changed about the lives that were lived there. Especially for girls, most of whom were looked at askance if they weren't wives and mothers before they were twenty, even now, after so many men had been lost in the war. Here, she was surrounded by women of her own age, living without any restraint of family or the conventional social expectations. It appeared none of them were earning much money, but at least it seemed they could chose how they lived, and loved. They didn't see themselves as selfish or unnatural. The realisation was intoxicating.

Jess was ushered into a small apartment strewn with underwear drying on lines stretched from one side of the room to the other.

'Cassie was looking for you,' called a girl emerging from one of the bedrooms. 'She wants us to go with her tonight.' She smiled. 'Hello, you must be Jess. I'm Vera; I work at Barringtons too, but in accounts, not the shop floor. Annette said she was bringing you back to stay with us.'

'If there's room,' said Jess, looking round the tiny space, carelessly strewn with books and magazines.

'Oh, there's plenty, don't worry. Sylvie's away until tomorrow, visiting her mother in Brighton. We can't throw you out when there's a bed free. Annette said you've come up all the way from Cornwall. That's much further than Brighton.'

'It feels like it,' replied Jess a little shyly.

'First time in London?'

'I've never even been to a city before.'

'Goodness me. I can't imagine living anywhere else. Do you like it?'

'I'm not sure,' said Jess, 'I haven't seen very much of it, although I love the energy and so many different people all thrown together. I didn't know anyone lived like this.'

Vera laughed. 'It's not all roses and champagne, I'm afraid. But I wouldn't be anywhere else. You've got to make the most of it while you're here. Why don't you come out with us tonight? It's at night this place really comes alive.'

Miss Fairbairn clucked like a mother hen. 'Jess has had a long day.'

'I'm not in the least tired now,' protested Jess. She might never have the opportunity to visit a place like London again. Now she was here, she wasn't going to miss this for the world.

'Then you've got to come. It's amazingly glamorous. You don't need money, there are plenty of men who'll buy you a drink if you just dance with them. Don't worry, we'll make sure they don't try to lure you away into their lairs.'

'Oh,' said Jess, feeling horribly unsophisticated and painfully aware of her total lack of luggage. She hadn't even a hairbrush. 'If you don't mind me going like this.'

'You can't possibly. No offence. But, really.' Vera looked at Jess critically. 'You're my size. A bit taller, but short dresses are fashionable nowadays. As long as it's just below the knee, you'll be perfectly respectable. I've got things I haven't even worn. The privilege of working next to the fashion department. Come on, we'll find you something.'

Annette looked at her anxiously. 'Jess, are you sure? Don't let yourself get bullied into this.'

'I might never have another chance.'

Within minutes, Jess was swept into a bedroom and dressed in more finery she'd ever seen in her life. Her blouse and skirt were replaced by a straight flow of apricot silk, waist dropped to around her hips and heavily beaded by coils of stylised leaves and flowers. Her hair was swept back into an approximation of the new short style, with a curve over her forehead, the remainder caught at the base of her neck.

She peered into the mirror in astonishment. 'Is that me?'

'Of course it is. Didn't anyone ever tell you you're beautiful?'

Jess eyed herself critically. She wasn't sure about the beautiful, but the gawkiness had vanished into the straight lines of the dress, and there was no trace of the blacksmith to be seen. 'I certainly look elegant.'

'I was going to lend you a necklace,' said Annette, 'but your pendant is so beautiful, you make mine look tawdry. I've never seen one like that. Where did you get it from?'

'I made it.'

'You made it?' Jess suddenly found every woman in the room crowding around her. 'I thought you were a seamstress?'

'That's how I earn my living, but this is my passion. I worked as a blacksmith during the war and since then I've been training in metalwork.'

'Well, I never.' Annette looked at her with new interest. 'I've heard of women working as blacksmiths, but I've never met one. Despite how horrible it all was and the Zeppelin raids, I really do miss driving trams. I'd love to have that independence again.'

'I wish I was still decoding messages for the War Office,' sighed Vera. 'It made me feel I was part of something bigger, that what I did really mattered.' She lowered her voice. 'Cassie from downstairs actually worked behind enemy lines. She can't tell us most of what she did, but she once let slip she led escaped prisoners of war over the Alps into Switzerland to avoid the border guards. I'm not sure she's finding it easy to settle back into civilian life.'

'Do you have a card?' asked Annette. 'A business card,' she explained, seeing Jess' bewildered look.

'No. I don't have my own workshop. I've had a few commissions, but they were mainly during the war. I'm working to be able to set up again soon.'

'Your commissions were for pendants, then?'

'The main one was for an enamelled hair clasp that could also be worn as a brooch or as the central piece of a headband.'

'A hair clasp? Of course! I should have remembered. I thought that enamelling looked familiar.' Vera disappeared into her bedroom, emerging minutes later with a page torn from a magazine, showing a young woman photographed in profile, abundant hair caught at the base of her neck by an ornamental clasp. 'Was it like this?'

Jess stared in astonishment. 'That's exactly like it.' She glanced at the caption. 'Yes, that's the name of the woman who bought it for her wedding. That must be the one. I didn't know it had been photographed.'

'This was from a party held a few months ago at the Savoy Hotel, which means she's still wearing it. It caught my eye because it was so beautiful and unusual. I was trying to work out what the colours might be. If they were anything like your pendant, it must look stunning.'

'They're almost exactly the same. I used the colours to make all the pieces form a set. The red was a little deeper in the final version, but that's about all.'

'Well, I never.' Annette looked up from the photograph. 'I remember seeing this. One of my private clients asked if Barringtons supplied anything like it. I'm forever trying to get Simms to take on more work by women, but he's such an old stick in the mud, he won't listen. He assumes it won't be of such good quality as that of a man, or the supply won't be as reliable because women are always being distracted by their domestic duties or love affairs. I've only stayed so long because I'm working on setting up my own emporium.' Her expression became thoughtful. 'If Barringtons give your aunt a contract to supply more fashion lines, you won't give this up, will you?'

'Never.'

Annette gazed back at the photograph. 'Do you think you could do another set like this one? Or something similar?'

'Yes, of course.'

'Could you get them to me within the next two weeks?'

'I'm sure I could,' said Jess, pushing the impossibility firmly away.

'The thing is, my private client who was so interested in the clasp is coming over from America in a few weeks. She's only staying a few days in London and I'd love to be able to show them to her. She was so interested in the photograph. She still wears her hair long, despite the fashion for the cropped look. It's become her trademark. She is always asking me to look out for dramatic ways to secure it.'

'It would be good publicity,' put in Vera. 'Her photograph is always in the newspapers these days. Annette's client is an actress in the moving pictures studios in Hollywood. She's famous. And very beautiful.'

'More to the point,' said Annette, 'women admire her and want to look like her, including the rich and fashionable, the kind of women I'll need to attract when I open my own emporium. Whatever she wears, other women follow. The last time she wore an evening dress from Barringtons to the opera, it sold out within days.'

'I'll get something to you as soon as I can,' said Jess, flickers of excitement bubbling up inside her. Just the recommendation of the bride for whom she had made the headband during the war had led to more commissions. A famous actress, who had her photograph in magazines and was a leader of fashion, could lead to so much more. In the far distance shone the tantalising hope that she might be able to set up her own workshop after all.

'I'm so glad I met you, Jess,' exclaimed Annette. 'This is just the kind of thing I've been looking for. Miss Harding has adored the things I've found for her, especially when they've been as unique as this. I'm hoping she'll agree to back me in setting up my emporium. Especially as I intend to specialise in unique and unusual pieces, the kind she loves and you generally have to look around for days to find. If I could get photographs of her wearing something so original, that could be just what I need to bring women in.'

How on earth she was going to make even a simple pendant, Jess had no idea. But she had stumbled on a chance, the only opportunity that might ever come her way to escape being confined to a sewing room for the rest of her life.

The rest of the evening was like nothing Jess had ever experienced before. They took a cab to the West End, to a smoky dance hall crammed with men and women dancing together to the fast, rhythmic music of a band quite different to anything she had heard. The women were dressed in similar sheaths of dresses to her own, in light fabrics, most barely covering their knees, and not a corset or flounced petticoat in sight. The dances seemed to involve a wild abandon she was quite sure she could never achieve in public, as she attempted to grasp the requirements of the exotically named foxtrot, the shimmy and the black bottom.

By the time they returned to crowd into Annette's apartment for toast, accompanied by wine splashed into teacups, Jess was worn out, but her mind was racing with all she had seen and heard. While the others chatted excitedly about the events of the evening, she curled into a corner with her notebook, sketching as much as she could remember of the décor, the shapes made by the exuberant dancers and the silhouettes of buildings in the streets outside.

'I've magazines as well,' said Annette, bringing her over a teacup of wine as Vera embarked on making toast and butter. 'There are photographs of society ladies showing their earrings and their fashions, if that will help.'

'Thank you,' Jess smiled. 'I'm not being rude, but I want to draw everything while it's fresh in my mind. I was wishing I could remember all the jewellery. They gave me so many ideas for patterns and I might never get another chance.'

'Stay for a few more days then,' said Annette. 'I'll swap with one of the other girls and get the afternoons off. There's an Art Deco exhibition near Trafalgar Square I can take you to, and there are several boutique shops run by women I'd love you to see. We can send another telegram to reassure Mrs Catchpole. After all, it's in my interest for you to have as many ideas as possible.'

Jess nodded. 'I'd like that, thank you.'

The next morning, as Jess and Annette made their way back to Barringtons, the other girls in the apartment had turned from their glamorous incarnations of the night before into their restrained working day clothes.

Even Cassie, when they passed her on the stairs, rushing out to her work as a clerk, wore a dark skirt reaching to just above the ankle and a severe-looking jacket, fair hair pinned back and almost hidden under her hat, as virginal as could be. She grinned when she saw then, before heading rapidly towards the nearest Underground station.

'Well?' demanded Annette, as they reached Mr Simms' office to find Mr Edwards poring over piles of paperwork. 'Did Simms come to a decision?'

Mr Edwards' smile was broad. 'Everyone agreed the quality was the best we've seen from a small supplier. To be honest, that embroidery alone is far superior to some of the pieces we stock from Paris fashion houses. You'll be pleased to know I've been tasked with drawing up the paperwork, Miss Morgan. The contract is yours.'

Jess sat down hard on the nearest chair, the tight knot in her stomach easing. 'Thank you, that's wonderful. My aunt will be delighted.'

'There, what did I tell you?' Annette beamed. 'I knew Barringtons wouldn't let work like that slip through its fingers to be snapped up by a rival. Now you have to stay, Jess. I'll arrange for a telegram to let your aunt know of your success and you are staying a couple of days to finalise the arrangements. You can't possibly go all the way back to Cornwall without some kind of celebration. And besides, there's so much I want to show you in London.'

'It would be good if you were able to stay for a few days,' added Mr Edwards. 'I've people I'd like you to meet, and we can discuss further possibilities while you are here. So much easier to throw around ideas and see where they land, I find, than by letter.'

'Yes of course,' said Jess. 'I'd love to, and I'm sure Aunt Sara would wish me to show you more of her ideas.'

She had watched Aunt Sara draw up several plans for new fashion lines to put before Barringtons, many of them featuring Morwenna's exquisite embroidery, all packed carefully inside her bag in case the opportunity to show them might arise. Aunt Sara was right: this could be the making of her new business and give Jess and Morwenna secure employment. Best of all, they would be able to stay in St Ives.

Jess breathed a sigh of relief. It meant she could continue

to develop her skills with Miss Catterell, and maybe even start to set up a studio of her own. She could contact the women who had shown interest in her designs—

Jess' plans came to sudden halt. How could she have forgotten? They might have secured the contract, but Aunt Sara's sewing room had gone up in flames, their equipment lost. How on earth were they going to fulfil the contract now? And if it proved impossible … Jess shut the idea from her mind. They'd find a way. They couldn't give up now.

For the rest of the morning, Jess was free to wander through Barringtons, trying to remain as inconspicuous as possible while taking everything in, furiously making notes of everything she had seen. Her notebook was soon full, her pencil worn to almost nothing. Just before lunch, she purchased the cheapest notebook and pencil she could find.

Barringtons was so huge and on so many floors it felt like a city in itself. She was mesmerised by row upon row of women's gowns and coats, shoes made from the finest leather, and jewellery made from precious stones that glinted in the electric lights. When Annette came to join her, she was peering warily at the cosmetic counter.

'They don't bite,' said Annette, laughing.

'I was just thinking how horrified Aunt Sara would be if I turned up at home wearing rouge and lipstick.'

'I can imagine,' replied Annette drily. 'I come from a tiny village in Somerset where nothing much has changed for centuries. Mum sees pierced ears as a mark of having sold my soul to the devil. I wouldn't dare wear rouge; it would bring shame on the entire family.' She sighed. 'Not that there are many young men there to lead into temptation, any more than there are in London. I'm not the only woman resigned to the fact that I'm not likely to be able to rely on a husband to support me. To be truthful, I'd rather spend my life as a businesswoman. I'm not in the least domestic and while I adore my sister's children, I've no great desire for my own. I fully intend to have a fruitful and happy life, and I don't consider myself to be surplus to requirements, not in any way.'

By the time Jess left London for the return journey to Cornwall, she had completely filled her second notebook with sketches and designs, and half-filled a third. Her mind buzzed with images from the Art Deco exhibition, followed by wandering whole rooms of paintings in the National Gallery. She had gaped at the opulence of the Ritz Hotel and seen the Houses of Parliament.

But even more exciting were the little shops run by young women not so very different from Annette, none of them likely to find a husband after the devastation of the war. Instead, some had thrown themselves into creating clothing, while others were designing for the clean lines of more modern interiors, stripped of their Victorian clutter. Many had appeared pale and strained, clearly struggling to make ends meet, but even more were already making a success of their little enterprise.

'That's the kind of place I'd like to use,' said Annette a little wistfully, as they passed a small building just off Oxford Street that, like so many, had been abandoned during the war. 'I know it would be a success; all many women need is a more prominent place to show their work. If Miss Harding agreed to back me, I'd leave Barringtons like a shot and set up my own place. And your hair clasp is one of the first things I'd stock.'

*

As her train headed west, leaving the sprawling city behind, Jess tried not to think of the practicalities of being able to take advantage of Aunt Sara's success with no premises or equipment, let alone her own unexpected opportunity.

She turned the pages of the magazine Annette had given her until she found the photographs of Miss Harding. Annette was right. The actress was arrestingly beautiful, with delicate features and huge eyes that looked out into the distance with an expression of such profound sadness Jess couldn't help a responsive lump forming in her own throat. The article accompanying the photograph was gushing about the star's beautiful home and exquisite taste. It didn't take much to work out that Giselle Harding was wealthy beyond Jess' wildest dreams.

Jess pushed the two filled notebooks even deeper inside her pockets, new determination coursing through her. She would help Aunt Sara to find a new place to work and make sure the commissioned gowns and coats were finished perfectly and on time, so that Sara could finally have the security of supplying Barringtons and begin to rebuild her business. But that wouldn't stop her from using every last ounce of energy to create the finest, most ingenious headband and hair clasp for Annette to show to Giselle Harding.

Jess opened the blank pages at the end of the third note-book and began to work feverishly on new designs. Whatever she made had to be so striking and original that everyone who saw it, even those who could only view it in black and white photographs, would instantly long to have a version of their own.

Jess sketched furiously away, ignoring curious glances from the other travellers in her compartment, refining the design over and over, making it just as she could envision it in her mind's eye. This was a huge opportunity, one that might never come again. Whatever happened, she wasn't about to let it slip through her fingers.

Chapter Sixteen

'He offered,' announced Louisa, a few days later.

Rachel turned from the window, where she had been gazing down into the harbour, banishing the longing from her face. 'Who did?'

'Tobias.' The triumphant expression on her sister's face turned to impatience. 'I told you he would.'

'And did you accept?'

'Of course not.' Louisa smoothed the arch of her eyebrows with her index finger with the aid of her reflection in the drawing-room window, her smile broadening into complacency.

'But you will.'

'Yes, of course. I'm not stupid. It doesn't do to allow a man to think you are desperate, you know.'

'Really.'

Louisa bristled. 'And why shouldn't I marry again?'

'If you believe he truly loves you and you love him.'

'Of course he does, why else would he ask?' There was a moment's silence. The colour slowly rose in Louisa's face. She ran her finger along the windowsill. 'Hannah hasn't dusted this in weeks.'

'Her grandmother is dying, hadn't you heard?'

'Mama should still speak to her.'

'Louisa!'

Louisa began to pout, then burst into tears. 'What else am

I supposed to do? I'm not like you, content to live your life in this backwater, doing good works to fill your time. I've got a chance to go to the theatre and parties and have nice things.'

'I thought you said the Howellses were unkind to you during the war.'

'Oh, that was a long time ago. I didn't know anything then. Mr Howells is very attentive each time I visit.'

'I'm sure he is.'

'What was that?'

'Nothing. Louisa, are you quite certain—'

'He does love me. Tobias, I mean. He says he doesn't mind me visiting here and staying with you and Mama as much as I please when we come down to the house in St Ives for the summer. He's promised to bring me here as often as I like. Of course, it makes sense – it will give him a chance to keep an eye on the harbour.'

'And why would he wish to do that?'

'To take care of my interests, our course.' She smiled. 'Our interests. And yours and Mama's too, of course. He can't just leave you to struggle on. He says there's so much more potential for the harbour, he wants to help the people in the cottages, too. He says they are in a terrible state, most barely fit for human habitation. He wants to bring them up to a good standard. A land fit for heroes, like they keep on saying in the newspapers.'

'But the cottages are nothing to do with him.'

Louisa shot her an impatient look. 'They will be when we're married. So, you see, my marrying him will be of benefit to you and Mama, too.'

Rachel opened her mouth, then shut it again. She could hear Tobias's voice feeding Louise the information he wished her to believe, bit by bit.

Unless she did something, she was quite sure Tobias would

persuade Mama that he should take complete control of the harbour and its inhabitants. She could just see him striding through, the self-styled emperor of his little domain, knowing there was no one to stand in his way.

Cook, whose cousin had been hired as undercook for the Howellses' villa in St Ives, had passed on whispers that young Mr Tobias barely lasted six months as manager of the Howellses' London warehouses before being unceremoniously replaced by his cousin Lucas and being packed off instead to the backwater of the Cornish coast to take over Peter's role of running the harbour.

'They said his father hauled him over the coals good and proper,' Cook had muttered darkly. 'Blood might be thicker than water, but nothing stands between old Mr Howells and profit, and if you don't come up to scratch ... Still smarting, if you ask me. I wouldn't like to be in the shoes of anyone who stands in his way.'

'Aren't you going to congratulate me?' demanded Louisa.

Rachel did her best, but she couldn't quite feign unbridled glee. 'I wish you to be happy, with all my heart.'

'But you mind. You wish it was you.'

'You don't believe that.'

Louisa bit her lip. 'I do love him. And I want to be married again. You don't know what it's like, to have all that taken away from you and have to live without a husband's love.'

'Then I wish you every happiness.' Rachel kissed Louisa, who rushed to tell their mother the news.

She could not win. Rachel turned to look back down into the harbour, where she could still make out Ben, sitting on the bench outside the forge in a pool of sunlight, gazing towards the far horizon, with the air of a man wrestling with despair.

Ben, at least the old Ben, the one she had fallen so

hopelessly and passionately in love with when nothing else in the world had mattered, would tell her she was wrong. He had been so certain, even in the midst of horror, that the rich and powerful didn't always win, however much they might believe it themselves and tell the world of their triumph. That was the real illusion, he said. In the end, power and wealth was nothing besides the small daily details that made up a life and really mattered.

He was right, she told herself, battling her own sense of hopelessness. For there had been hope in among the despair, in the tightly-knit band of doctors and nurses and volunteers who had come from all walks of life, risking everything in the struggle to alleviate the horror and keep hope alive. The kindness was what she remembered, in the midst of the suffering. Lives, which in the vast sweep of time would always be brief, meeting each other at the extremes, sharing the most intense moments of life that, even at its most terrible, had felt a privilege. It had been a time of madness, but also of the profoundest truth.

A deep ache had set up inside her. For all the battleground's terror, she would have stepped back there in an instant. She tore her eyes away from the figure on the bench as her mother joined her at the window seat.

'I take it Louisa informed you of her news, my dear.'

'I'm afraid I offended her by not being sufficiently enthusiastic,' replied Rachel guiltily.

'I rather think I was a little the same.' Mrs Bellamy sighed. 'I know Louisa will only be happy with a husband, and I have tried to put aside any personal feelings on the matter. But at least with Peter, although we were all aware that he was marrying her for the sake of the partnership between our families, there was a sense that he would always try to act honourably and never deliberately hurt her. The trouble is, this time I feel she is so desperate, she's ignoring her own better instincts. I can find no sign that she loves Tobias in any way, or has even thought much about what her life might be like as his wife. I don't want to see her making a mistake that would imprison her for the rest of her life. We simply don't have the financial resources to free her, should the worst come to the worst. But I have no power to stop her. It seems there is no other choice. And it does need a man to run the harbour.'

'Does it? Are you so sure? And besides, do you really think Tobias will have the best interests of the harbour, or its inhabitants, at heart?'

'My dear, it will take someone practical, who understands business, to ensure the harbour can survive at all. We truly would not have survived without the Howells, and that was before the war. I really can't see what else we can do. At least this way the harbour will get the investment it needs.'

'Maybe,' said Rachel thoughtfully. She turned her gaze back down to the figure on the bench. She would never admit it, but she still had a stake in the harbour. Ben was avoiding her, just as she was avoiding him. Whatever they might have shared out in France had been lost for ever in the return to normality and the impossible social gulf between them. But the least she could do for Ben was to give him some future.

She was all too painfully aware that in the world outside the harbour, he would be just another of those unable to work due to their war injuries. Without the chance to find ways of overcoming his disability and finding hope again, he would certainly be reduced to poverty and a life of dependency and humiliation.

She couldn't stay here as the maiden aunt to Louisa's children, subject to every petty dig and barbed comment Tobias chose to throw at her, just to keep a roof over her head. She knew him well enough to guess how much he would revel in her dependency. Even the petty tyranny of Aunt Julia would be better than that, and in a city like Birmingham she would stand a better chance of finding some kind of employment. But before she made her own bid for freedom, she could fight for the harbour and give it a chance. Give Ben a chance. It was the only thing she had left.

Part Three

—

1921

Chapter Seventeen

A few days after her return, Jess stepped out of the cottage, Dad's lunch of bread and cheese in her hand, and breathed in deep the sea air.

It was strange being back in the little harbour after the months in the bustle of St Ives and the intensity of her days in London. The truth was, the time away had made her love more than ever the peace of the tightly-knit community where she knew she belonged. She had missed the greetings of their neighbours and the gentle lap of the sea against the harbour wall.

All the same, she couldn't help but notice how empty the harbour seemed. Since her last visit, yet another business next to the quay had given up the fight to meet the new rents and had moved away in search of more customers.

Aunt Sara had been delighted at the success of the visit to Barringtons, with the potential of attracting further business as her reputation spread. But without premises, she wouldn't be able to rebuild what had been lost, let alone take advantage of the chance they had worked night and day to win.

So near and yet so far. Jess itched to get going on her own designs, now drafted to her satisfaction in her notebook. The obvious choice would be to ask to use Diana's workshop. But without her work in the sewing room, she had no means of staying in St Ives or buying the materials she needed. Already several days of the two weeks had gone.

She hadn't said anything to Dad or Aunt Sara. The new order from Barringtons for Aunt Sara was a certainty, not a shot in the dark that might come to nothing. Providing original jewellery designs for Annette's emporium might be her opportunity to be able to support herself in the long run, but the reality was that Annette might never leave Barringtons and they needed to secure an immediate income. Dad's earnings alone were not enough to keep the three of them for longer than a few weeks, and if the rumours were true about Tobias Howells being engaged to Miss Louisa, she had a feeling Dad wouldn't retain his post for long.

Jess sighed. She missed Frank's presence more than she could say. She had grown so used to him being only a few streets away in St Ives and seeing him almost every day as they walked on the beach or accompanied Charlotte to her drawing lessons. Frank would have understood and helped her to find a solution – he knew just how much this chance meant.

They'd only spoken briefly as he helped her and Morwenna to retrieve anything that could be of use from the burnt-out workshop under Aunt Sara's anxious gaze. She wasn't sure when she would see him or Charlotte again.

The treadle machine had been salvageable, as had the buttons and thread in containers, but the rest was lost. Even worse, the whole street had been declared unsafe after the destruction caused by just a single untended candle, and Aunt Sara had yet to find a suitable replacement in St Ives.

'There are so many artists renting spaces,' Dad had said, when Aunt Sara had wearily returned to the harbourmaster's cottage yesterday afternoon, after she and Jess had spent a day searching fruitlessly.

'I'm sorry, Jess, after all that you've done,' Sara had said gloomily, 'but I have no choice but to let Barringtons know that I can't fulfil their order.'

Without her work with Aunt Sara, Jess would have to find other employment, any employment, as soon as possible. She had seen plenty of advertisements for cleaners and kitchen work at the hotels and guesthouses in St Ives, while many private households all along the coast were crying out for maids. But there was a reason so few girls wanted to be a maid, with grinding hard work every hour of the day, no evenings free and living at the whim of your employers. Cleaning work was paid so poorly she would have to take on several jobs and work all hours to make ends meet, cleaning and washing dishes until she was too worn down and exhausted to even begin her own work.

She had worked hard for Aunt Sara, but she'd had her evenings free to pursue her metalwork and meet up with Frank and Charlotte. At least she'd had a few hours each day to live her own life. She hated the thought of her whole existence being one of drudgery solely for the benefit of others.

As she reached the door to the harbourmaster's office, she turned to watch the painter with the damaged hand, who was back on the harbour wall working *en pleine aire*, as the artists of St Ives liked to call it. Today, he had been joined by several other painters, equally absorbed.

'Aye, they've been here the past week, while it's been fine,' said Dad, coming out into the sunshine to join her. 'Looks like word has spread. There's plenty more coming each week. There's that woman with a photographic camera too, one of those folding things that takes more than one picture at a time, or so she says. Don't ask me how. She's got some studio where she processes them. She always smells of vinegar, or some such thing. Must be the chemicals.'

'I'm glad they find it worth painting and photographing.'

'Picturesque, that's what the fellow on the harbour calls it.' Dad sounded dubious. 'Doesn't see it as a place of work, or where people are struggling. They sees what they want to see, if you ask me. Quite blind to what's really there.'

'Or knowing what will sell.'

'A smelly old harbour?'

'The people I met in London couldn't believe I lived so close to the sea, surrounded by cliffs and fields. Most of them were envious. You should see the dirt and hear the noise there, Dad. It never stops and there are so many people, most of whom never speak to each other. No wonder they see a place like this as paradise.'

'Well, I wouldn't go that far.'

'You know its darker side,' she replied, kissing him. 'But even you'd admit you wouldn't want to live anywhere else.'

'Given half a chance,' he replied, with a sigh.

As Jess reached the forge, Mrs Wilkes was sitting outside in the warmth of the sunshine, with the first hint of spring in the air, enjoying a cup of tea. The smithy was still and silent. There were no horses waiting patiently to be shod, just rows of gates and railings waiting to be mended. A ghost of a place that had once been the hub of the harbour for as long as anyone could remember.

'So, you came.'

'You sound as if you were expecting me, Mrs Wilkes.'

'I knew you couldn't stay away, love, once you were back.'

'Oh.' Jess swallowed. 'I only wanted to ask Ben if I could borrow a few tools. Not the best ones. I promise I'll replace them as soon as I can. I've a couple of pieces I want to make. I'll find a place I can use as a workshop.'

'In that case, why not use this one?' She turned to find Ben leaning against the doorframe.

'I couldn't.'

'Why not?'

'I don't want to make trouble for you.'

'Well,' remarked Mrs Wilkes, 'seems to me, trouble has come, whether we wants it or not.'

Ben was still watching her. 'What are these pieces you want to make?'

'One of the women at Barringtons in London said they'd look at my enamel work if I sent it to her. She may be able to find an opening for me. I know it's a long shot, but I've got to at least try. But if I can't do it soon, it'll be too late.'

'Barringtons, eh?' She saw his good fist clench, then deliberately unclench. 'They have branches all over the place. This could be the making of you, Jess.'

'It's not for Barringtons. It's for a woman who's hoping to start up her own emporium. So it may come to nothing.'

'Even so, that's the kind of chance that doesn't come again, Jess. So why waste time when there's a perfectly good workshop here?'

'Like I said, I don't want to cause trouble. If Tobias Howells hears your workshop is being used, I'm sure he'll persuade Mrs Bellamy to put up the rent on the forge, especially now there's a garage in St Ives to mend their motor cars.'

'Aye,' said Ben. 'We've not had a motor car in here for months.' He cleared his throat. 'I went to that garage in St Ives a few days ago. It seemed worth a try. I can still do some mechanics, and there's not many men here who have the experience. But it didn't do me any good. They're like the rest. They don't want to employ a man with only one good hand, who takes longer than the youngest apprentice, even though I might do the job better in the end.'

'They might at least have given you a trial,' said his mother angrily.

He shook his head. 'Why would anyone want to employ someone who is a daily reminder of the war and all that was lost? I've worked all my life, from helping Dad after school to the day I left for France. Now I'm on the scrapheap.'

'I know you'll find something,' said Jess, 'but all the more reason for me not to cause trouble for you.'

'Tobias Howells is just looking for an excuse,' returned Ben. 'You can tell whenever he walks through the harbour, whenever he visits Enys Hall, and that's become every few days, just lately. He knows there isn't enough work for the forge to keep going. We can barely make the rent as it is, and that's with Morwenna working day and night packing fish, and handing over all of her earnings to keep us going. I'm not going to let her slave away to keep me.'

'You does what yer can,' said Mrs Wilkes frowning.

'But Morwenna should be working on her embroidery, not packing fish. If it's true Tobias is going to marry Rachel's sister, he must know all he has to do is wait his chance and none of us will be able to hold out against him. There's a rumour the Howells want to expand the munitions side of their business that made them a fortune during the war. There's still plenty out there willing to buy armaments. It's a nice, discreet, out-of-the-way place here, with direct access to the sea. I'd say Tobias has his instructions. It sounds like he's failed at everything else he's tried, so I'm sure he'll do everything he can to succeed here. From what I've see of Mr Howells, he isn't one to accept failure.'

'What the lad means,' remarked Mrs Wilkes, eyes on the

distant horizon, 'is that we'm nothing to lose. Backs to the wall. Same with all of us left in the harbour. Whatever we do, you can see young Howells is bent on getting rid of us.'

'So why not use here?' said Ben.

'Tobias could still make life difficult for you.'

'We'll cross that bridge when we come to it. Tobias is banking on fear of what he might do driving us apart. He knows that none of us left here can risk losing a home or an income: we might never get another and be in the workhouse in Penzance before we know it.'

'Thing is,' remarked Mrs Wilkes, 'anyone who *can* get out of the harbour has gone. Us who's left don't have no choice. Back to the wall can make even the smallest of creatures dangerous.'

Jess hesitated.

'You've got to take this chance, Jess,' urged Ben. 'It might never come again. If you don't try, how will you ever know? And Mum's right. The harbour is bound to be cleared of the workshops so they can be used for greater profits, whatever we do.'

'Very well.' She took a deep breath. 'But only if you work too, Ben.'

'Jess...'

'Why not? It's your life. It's what you've always loved doing ever since I used to watch you as a little girl. You may find, like with the mechanics, you can learn a way round things, so you can work again, or at least be able to teach.'

'That's not a certainty, Jess.'

She had always been able to match him in stubbornness. 'But it would mean we could put it about that I'm simply being a good angel and helping you get back to being able to use your hand again. In a therapeutic manner, I mean. There's been plenty of that since the war. I'm sure Miss Rachel would back me up, if I asked.'

'There's no need for that,' he said sharply.

'Asking won't do any harm.'

'No.' He sounded almost angry. She'd never seen him dig his heels in for no good reason and so against his own interest before. At the back of her mind something stirred. Ben hadn't said anything about his time in France, not even to his mother. That wasn't unusual: none of them did. But she did know that many of the volunteers who had gone out from the harbour and St Ives, Quakers or not, had been directed towards the same field hospital.

She glanced up towards Enys Hall. Surely not. It was impossible. She was letting her imagination run away with her. Besides, they all had far more pressing matters to deal with. She dragged her attention back to the present.

'Jess is talking sense about trying to work,' Mrs Wilkes was saying. 'You might as well try, love, even if it's not for long. You won't be happy until you do.'

Jess could see him wavering. 'It would only be for a week, or a few days more, at most,' she put in quickly. 'If I don't get the pieces Miss Fairbairn is interested in on time, I'll have missed my best chance. While if she takes them ...'

'You might be in a position to set up your own workshop,' Ben finished for her.

'Yes.'

'Then I could come and work for you,' he added, bitterness in his voice.

'I didn't mean that.' His face was shut in on itself once more. Despair went through her. She'd so wanted to help, but now it seemed she had only made things worse. 'I'd better get back, Aunt Sara will be expecting me.'

'But you'll come tomorrow,' said Mrs Wilkes anxiously.

'Take no notice of Ben – he'll do his best to help you.' She frowned at her son. 'And it's only fer a few days.'

'I'm not sure, Mrs Wilkes.'

'You'd better be early,' said Ben abruptly. 'I'll have a look through tonight, sort out what's there. If you are to get that work done in time, you'll need to start straight away. I can't be letting you send in a shoddy piece. So be here as soon as you can,' he added, disappearing into the house.

Jess met Mrs Wilkes' eyes, to find them flooded with tears. 'Well, and he ain't shown that amount of life since he's been back.'

'I'll be here tomorrow,' she replied firmly. Inside, her heart was performing handsprings, her mind too full of all she had to do to consider anything else. All that mattered for now was that at last she had a chance.

Ben was as good as his word. By the time Jess arrived in the workshop the next morning, he had already cleared the workbench and was sorting out the containers of powdered glass.

'There's most colours here, still.'

'I can't use your materials!'

'Whyever not? No one else is using them. No point in wasting your savings when I can't see myself doing such fine work again.' He held out his good hand for the paper in her hand. 'So what's this design you're making?'

'It's a hair clasp. I got the idea from the one your dad mended for Mrs Bellamy when I was a girl. It can be taken apart so it can be worn as a brooch, or around the hair as part of a headband. I've changed the original decoration, so it's more in the Art Deco style, like the things Miss Fairbairn showed me in London, but the mechanism is still similar to one I made during the war.'

'Morwenna told me about that.' As he inspected the rays of sun streaming out between cloud, illuminating the sails of a tiny boat, his face was alight with the passion she had seen all her life and had feared she would never see again. 'Yes, you're right. That's perfect for the Art Deco style. What colour were you thinking for the sail?'

'As near to gold as I can get it. I don't want the piece to look gaudy, but if the rest are deep blues for the sea, and mauves and crimsons for the cliffs and the sun's rays, that should make the boat stand out. As if caught in the sunset. I want it to be calm, with a touch of sadness, but also hopeful. If that makes sense.'

He nodded. 'Aye, I can see what you mean.'

'The client Miss Fairbairn is thinking of has fair hair, so I need to use colours that will stand out but also compliment her colouring.'

He nodded. 'I see what you mean. I'm sure there are some colours here that will suit. I'll sort some out for you.' He caught the look on her face. 'Don't worry, I won't interfere.'

'I didn't think—'

'Yes, you did. And you were quite right. Once a teacher, always a teacher. The bench is yours.' He coughed. 'Besides, I'll be too busy on my own work. You are right, Jess. It's time I face this, and see if I can do anything at all.'

Over the next week, Jess slipped into the workshop every minute she could.

However exhausted she was, however much her eyes ached and her fingers were stiff from the mending Aunt Sara had managed to secure to give them some form of income while they still struggled to find new premises and the equipment they needed to start the work for Barringtons, she felt new energy flowing through her the moment she took her work out of its hiding place.

It was strange having Ben working at the next bench again. She could see him trying to figure out ways of manoeuvring with his undamaged hand, to make the tools work in an unfamiliar way. He brushed aside any hesitant attempt to help, muttering about time being too short, pride in every inch of his stance as he turned away from her, hiding his clumsy actions as he struggled with an old piece of pewter. After a few attempts, she left him to it. He might have generously surrendered the position of tutor, but she could sense how he hated to be in the position of pupil.

She had so little time, she couldn't afford to think. She was thankful for Ben's understanding that she needed to concentrate and his lack of any attempt to engage her in anything but the briefest of conversation.

'You've come a long way,' remarked Ben, as they began work a few mornings later. 'Art Deco was the style just beginning to come in when I was in Birmingham. I always thought of it as cold. Mechanical. You've made it beautiful.'

'I saw so much of it when I was in London. I wanted to make sure this is fashionable, as well as unique, so someone would be proud to wear it.'

'When did you become the canny businesswoman?'

'Diana Catterell in St Ives taught me that, when I worked in her silversmith workshop. I can't afford to be an artist. This is survival. It's the only way I'm ever going to be able to spend my life doing something I love while making enough money so I don't have to spend all hours at that sewing machine for the rest of my life. So I need to make something people know they couldn't buy anywhere else.'

'Like a signature.'

'I suppose. Yes.'

'Good for you. I'm afraid I may have looked down on commercial pieces when I was at the Birmingham School of Jewellery. I always made what pleased me, rather than anyone else.'

'You make me feel grubby.'

He gave the wryest of chuckles. 'Don't forget, I was looking forward to the luxury of a teacher's salary to support me. I might not have been so superior if I'd had to pay my rent from what I sold.'

She hated the raw pain in his voice. 'You could still teach, Ben.'

'Who wants to be taught by me? No. That's over. I need to find some other way of earning a living.'

All the same, the next day the copper vase that had stood covered in dust since he had left for France had been cleaned and moved onto a lower shelf. The following day, its shape had changed. Very subtly but unmistakably. Within days, the pewter had been abandoned, while the vase remained permanently on Ben's workbench, along with an array of broken necklaces that had lain in a small tin, abandoned by their owners.

They still said very little. With so little time left, Jess put all her concentration into her own work, leaving Ben to continue his struggle for ways of making his damaged fingers obey his commands and get round the obstacles posed by stumps of where fingers had once been. All the same, it was a companionable silence, like it had been when they'd worked together before the war. She found herself not wanting it to end.

The clasp was almost completed, and the accompanying pendant taking shape, when the sound of raised voices disturbed their peace.

'I don't care what your orders might be, young man,' Mrs

Wilkes was saying loudly. 'You're not disturbing my son. He's ashamed enough as it is, him with half his hand missing and his head not right. Doctor's orders, this is. Doctor's orders. You ask Dr Galbraith from St Ives. Hero, my son is.'

'Mrs Wilkes.' The man sounded exasperated, clearly having been harried from the moment he stepped foot in the forge. 'You informed Mrs Bellamy that your workshop was no longer in use, due to your son's disability. The family were very generous towards you, in recognition of your son's actions during the war. But Mr Tobias is concerned that such generosity is being abused. He does not wish a widow like Mrs Bellamy to be taken advantage of because she is a woman. I am charged with speaking to him.'

Jess hastily shoved the pendant into her pockets, while Ben pushed the hair clasp and the copper vase high up on the top shelf, behind a row of half-finished jugs.

'Well, I never.' There was an undisguised leer as the man pulled open the door. 'So this is the kind of work you are undertaking now, Wilkes. Very pretty.'

Ben's good fist clenched.

'Don't be daft, Mr Price,' said Mrs Wilkes. 'Jess is an old friend. Like a daughter she is to me, and don't you forget it. I won't have no aspersions cast on my family, or you won't hear the last of it.'

Mr Price ignored her. 'Helping you work, eh, Wilkes?'

'I can hardly work,' replied Ben. 'Miss Morgan has been kind enough to help me be able to gain strength in my hands again, not produce anything.'

'He's doing his best,' said Jess, pulling out the piece of pewter Ben had worked over again and again in an attempt to get his damaged hand to obey him and which was unmistakably clumsy. 'I've heard they had injured soldiers doing embroidery during the war. It seemed metalwork might be equally therapeutic, as well as helping Ben regain the use of his injured hand.'

'Indeed.' The newcomer's eyes were travelling over the shelves, seeking out anything that might be seen as new work. He lifted down a few of the teapots nearest to him, inspecting them closely. Thankfully, they were still untouched and covered in dust.

He was getting near to the clasp. Jess's heart began to bang uncomfortably in her chest. If he found that, he would be sure to report back to Tobias, who would know what they were up to. It didn't matter if they naturally assumed it was Ben; it was so clearly a commercial piece it would be all the excuse Tobias would need. What had she done accepting Ben's offer of using the workshop? Even the smallest increase in rent would mean the Wilkeses would be out on the street.

'This is what I've been working on,' said Ben, handing Mr Price the pewter. 'Better than my first attempt. But you can see yourself it's not anywhere near the standard anyone would buy. Take it to show Mr Howells; that should satisfy him.'

Mr Price placed the metal in his pocket. 'We'll see what Mrs Bellamy says about this. She might yet see it as commercial usage.'

'I'm sure Mrs Bellamy wouldn't wish one of her tenants to be a cripple and a burden on the parish,' put in Jess quickly. 'She could hardly wish for a man who has lost so much saving the lives of so many brave soldiers on the front line to be forced to abandon his attempts to be able to acquire gainful employment. And I'm quite certain Mr Howells would not wish to see him forced to apply for charity.'

'I …' Mr Price, who was only just young enough to have narrowly avoided being sent out to France himself, wavered.

'I wouldn't. Up to Mr Howells.' With a curt nod, he shot out through the door.

'He'll be back,' said Ben, watching through the window to make sure their visitor was heading back up towards the road to St Ives.

'He will that,' replied his mother. 'He were asking me all kinds of questions.'

'About me?' said Jess.

'He were more interested in what Ben were doing.'

'This is my fault,' said Jess.

'But I'd never have tried to get back to being able to work and find out how much I can do with my left hand,' said Ben. 'They'd have always found some excuse.'

She looked in despair at the pendant. 'That means there will be even less time to get these done.'

'Then you'd better get on with them,' said Ben, sounding severe as he reached down the hair clasp from its hiding place. 'I'm not letting you give up now.'

As she opened the door to the cottage later that day, Jess found Aunt Sara scrubbing the kitchen table with her good arm, with the air of a woman giving vent to her feelings.

'Still no luck?'

'Nothing. He must have heard I was planning to employ people from the harbour, that money was going back into the place, which would have meant the Bellamys would never sell out to them.' She sat down wearily, brows drawn tight together in pain. 'I'm too old for this.'

'You are supposed to be resting and getting well. I'll make us some tea.' Jess pushed the kettle back onto the range and reached for the teapot on the shelf. 'We could try Truro or Penzance. And there might still be somewhere in St Ives we haven't found yet. There has to be somewhere that will rent out a workspace. There has to be some solution.'

'Thanks to you, there is.'

'Me?'

Sara took a crumpled envelope from her pocket, the Barringtons crest embossed on one side. 'This arrived this morning.'

'You wrote and told them we couldn't do the work.'

'I'm afraid there was nothing else I could do, my dear. It's been clear for days we'll never get back into a position of being able to complete the order on time. Better be straight with them now, rather than let them down later. At least I can keep my professional pride.'

'But I thought you said it was good news?'

'It is. On the strength of our work, Mr Simms has offered me a post with Barringtons, in their design department. I'd be working on their new fashions.'

'Oh.' Jess digested this. 'I thought you didn't want to work for someone else.'

'I can't see any other way. This could allow me to earn enough to start my own business again in a year or two. And, to be honest, I would be in a better position to make more contacts if I'm in London.' Sara spread the letter on the table. 'They are interested in employing you as well. It would be a good opening. With your sewing skills, you would have the chance to rise to earn a reasonable wage and build a new life for yourself.'

A tightness squeezed her chest. 'I can't just leave Dad.'

'Sweetheart, there's no work here in the harbour. It's bound to get worse when Tobias marries Miss Louisa and properly takes over, just as Mr Peter would have done. Whatever happens, you are going to have to move away to earn any kind of living. Between us, we'd be able to earn enough to rent a place large enough for Tom as well. Him and your mum were good to me when I was left with nothing; I don't know what I'd have done if they hadn't taken me in. I would never abandon him, any more than you.'

'But Dad's life is here.'

'I'm afraid, the way things are, he may have no choice. Unless one of us can earn a living, we could all soon end up in the workhouse.' She gave a final scrub of the table and sat down, exhausted by the effort, wincing as she jerked her injured arm. 'Darling, I don't see what other choice there is. You've become a good little seamstress. Even if I'm not able to set up my own company again, work with Barringtons would set you up for life. I'll write to them in the morning. I've done my best, but there's nothing for us here, not any more.'

Chapter Eighteen

'So it seems we are to be brother and sister again,' remarked Tobias, joining Rachel as she attacked the garden a few days later. Rachel straightened, pushing fallen strands of hair away from her face with the back of her hand.

'So it does.'

'How very delightful.' His eyes strayed past her to rest on the harbour below. 'I expect we shall be seeing far more of each other from now on. Louisa always feels happy here. I hope to spend far more time at Enys Hall once we are married.'

'Indeed.' She returned to pruning the stems of the nearest rose. He was standing a little too close, in an undisguised attempt to force her to step back and give way to his masculine power. That was how it would always be from now on: Tobias slowly, stealthily, exerting his influence over all of them.

She'd met men like Tobias among the hierarchy that kept control of the army and the nursing staff, both here and in France. Most of the men and women were dedicated to their work, every last morsel of energy concentrated on doing their jobs. But there was always one puffed-up little man, nothing more than a domestic tyrant at home, revelling in the opportunity to be a small god in the ordering of supplies and ambulances. Men who used all that strutting and bluster to conceal their weakness, playing the strong man, relentlessly bullying anyone who might threaten their position, even if it was simply by competence.

There had been some women, too, who had mercilessly harried the nurses under their care, as no doubt they did their maids at home. But it was the men she remembered most. Maybe because the ordering of the world meant that they were the only ones with any real power.

A little half-smile appeared on Tobias's face. 'I'm surprised nothing has been done.'

'Done?'

'With the harbour. Everyone is saying how much it has declined since your father died. You can see from here it is barely surviving. Papa is most concerned for the investment the Howells put into the place to keep Leviathan alive. Considerable investment.' Rachel just managed to contain a snort at this outright lie. He was taking her for a fool. 'Not to mention purchasing the land on the far side. That represents a considerable investment in itself. Your father assured us when Peter agreed to buy the meadows that the harbour had a solid financial future. But now there really needs to be more dredging, or the place will completely silt up. It's happened to several harbours around the coast, which have had to be abandoned, their buildings becoming worthless. A few more years and trading vessels won't be able to navigate the harbour at all, and then where will we be?'

'Oh,' said Rachel. She felt certain most of this was a blatant lie too, Tobias feeling secure in her ignorance of the workings of a harbour. She could feel him unsettling her, establishing his superior masculine knowledge, making her doubt her own mind. He was already laying the groundwork for undermining everything she said and any objections she might ever have to his future plans.

How Louisa could fool herself she would ever have a

peaceful life, let alone happiness, with a man who didn't care to conceal his contempt for the female sex, and thought he could barge his way through anything, was beyond her. Surely no material security was worth this? She'd seen too often how petty bullies were prepared to destroy lives and minds in their pursuit of an illusion of power, trampling underfoot any they believed might stand in their way.

Having made his point, Tobias turned to make his way back towards the house.

'You're right, of course,' she said briskly. 'The harbour does need investment. Perhaps Mama needs to reconsider its future. For one thing, a reduction in the rents for the workshops would encourage businesses to return. Times are still hard for many after the war.'

'My dear Rachel, you could hardly expect Leviathan to undercut itself and be taken advantage of. It's a business. As I informed your mother, the rents on the workshops are simply market rents. I applaud your charitable nature, but we must be realistic. You have to understand that the rents pay for the upkeep of the buildings and the harbour.'

'But not if they lie empty. Surely some rent is better than none at all?'

'The matter has been considered thoroughly.' With a dismissive wave of the hand, he turned back towards the house.

She gritted her teeth. Louisa might hate her until the end of their days, but this was a matter of survival. 'You will have to deal with us, you know, even if you are married to Louisa.'

'My dear lady...'

'Perhaps you need to speak to Mama. It's better to have things clear and out in the open before the legal niceties are finalised, don't you think? Just so you know where you really stand.'

The air of patronising gallantry vanished into a scowl. 'What the hell are you talking about?'

'My father changed his will after Oliver died.'

'Changed?'

'He heard something about Peter. Don't mistake me, he was still fond of him, but he no longer fully trusted him to have our best interests at heart. Mine and my mother's in particular.'

'What sort of thing?'

'That he had a particular reason for spending so much time in London.'

'That bloody woman. I warned Peter she'd cause trouble.'

'On the contrary, Miss Harding has never contacted any of us. To be honest, I rather like her for it.'

'Has your family no pride whatsoever? No wonder no man has ever looked at you twice.'

'But it's not reprehensible for a man to marry a woman he knows he will never love because his father instructs him he needs a business partnership to secure control of a private harbour?'

'You little …' He took a step towards her.

'It's no good striking the messenger, Tobias. And whatever you do to me, I won't keep quiet. I've watched friends die in my arms and seen others horribly mutilated. Haven't they told you I'm the madwoman who walks across the cliffs, who no longer cares for life? I've already lost too much for you to be able to threaten me.'

That last bit was her own bit of bluster. The veneer of contempt that had been aimed at intimidating her was gone, leaving undisguised loathing. Well, at least they both knew where they stood.

'So I suggest,' she continued, 'that you speak to my mother before you make arrangements at the church. Just so you know exactly what you are getting yourself into. My father made sure that Louisa isn't able to give her husband any legal control over the future of the harbour, and if she marries again she gives up any interest in Enys Hall too. The day-to-day running is all you'll ever be able to take responsibility for, just as Peter would have done had he and Oliver survived. And if you think you can bully us into handing over anything more just because we are women, you've got another think coming.'

She was shaking as she watched him stride towards the house, fury in every step. Papa might have been the one to do his best to protect the harbour, but she was the one Tobias would find it convenient to blame. She shuddered. She had revealed something of her true self to Tobias, who was the kind of man who divided females into useful, irrelevant, and hags fit only for the ducking stool.

She was well aware that being irrelevant had so far kept herself safe from any kind of attention. Tobias reached the house, slamming the door behind him.

Now that safety was gone.

'How could you?'

Rachel had known the storm was coming from the moment she'd heard Tobias's Bentley roaring down the drive, gravel flying.

'He'd have found out in the end, Louisa. Surely better now than later. If he truly loves you, he won't mind that you keep control of your part of the harbour even after you are married, and you will no longer have any stake in the house even when Mama dies.'

'It's only because you're jealous,' said Louisa sullenly. 'I'd willingly give Tobias my part of the harbour.'

Rachel stared at her in disbelief. Had she just made Tobias

view her as an enemy to be punished for nothing? 'And leave me and Mama to have to fight him and the rest of the Howells? All those men and that money against two women? Don't you care about us at all, Louisa?'

'Of course I care about you. That's a horrible thing to say. What are you going to do with the harbour, anyhow? Tobias knows what he's talking about. He understands business.'

'No more than Mama, or you and I if we cared to study it. None of us would have driven all those little businesses that have been there for generations out of the harbour.'

'But Tobias says, if they can't pay the market rents ...'

'Oh, for goodness sake, Louisa. Listen to yourself. God gave you a brain, so use it. Don't just parrot what a man says because he says it.'

'Women simply aren't capable ...' Louisa faltered at her sister's expression.

'I'm sure Tobias finds it very convenient to believe women's inner organs will shrink to nothing if they use their brains, and they will need to be confined to a lunatic asylum if they dare to think. But that doesn't hold water any more. I worked under women running field hospitals in France and believe me, they were neither weak nor stupid, despite many of the officials persisting in treating them as inferior creatures. At least the men out there treated me like a fellow human being.'

'Then you should have stayed.'

'Maybe I should. Believe me, if things had been different, I'd never have returned. But that wouldn't have changed things. Tobias had to find out some time that Papa had taken steps to protect me and Mama.'

'But now he won't want to marry me.'

'If he loved you, surely it wouldn't matter about the harbour? You can't still want to marry him, surely?'

'Of course I do. I don't care. And I'll tell him it's just you being horrible, because you wanted him for yourself all along.'

'Don't you dare!'

Louisa sniffed loudly. 'Well, it's true.'

'Oh, for goodness sake. Tell him whatever you like.'

There was a moment's silence. 'I won't,' said Louisa at last, in a small voice. 'Tell him, that is. And I know it's not true. Not really.'

'I know you won't.' Rachel put her arms around her, feeling Louisa sob against her. 'I don't want us to squabble. Heaven knows, we've done enough of that in our lives.'

Louisa's hiccup turned into a watery giggle. 'Mama used to say we'd argue over stones on the beach, given half a chance.'

'Well, it's true,' said Rachel, kissing her. 'I know we see things differently, especially when it comes to Tobias, but surely we can come to some kind of compromise? I want you to be happy, darling, but I need to know Mama's future is secure too.'

Louisa blew her nose. With her face blotchy and her hair awry, her beauty had softened into a loveliness that was missing when she was trying with every last sinew in her body to play the fine lady. Rachel longed from the bottom of her heart to keep her that way, to have some means of showing Louisa that there were so many other paths she could take, and that men would always fall at her feet.

But already her sister was smoothing her hair, her face settling back into elegance. 'I will marry him. I'm not giving this up, not for anyone.'

'But there are still good men out there. They might not be rich, but if they are good and kind and love you, surely they could still make you truly happy.'

Louisa fished out her heavily laced handkerchief and blew her nose loudly, in the most unladylike fashion. 'Maybe I should just be a mistress. That seems to be the best way of getting on in life, after all. And being loved.'

Rachel's heart clenched. 'Louisa?'

A copy of *Vogue* magazine was thrown at her feet. When she picked it up, it was still open at the page that had been lying in front of her sister. There was no mistaking the beautiful woman at its centre, gazing wistfully into an imagined distance, the soft light and shade of the studio photograph enhancing the delicacy of her features. 'Oh. I see. I'm so sorry.'

'So you knew all about her as well. Like everyone else. Just laughing at me, all the time.'

'That was cruel of Tobias.'

'Tobias didn't tell me. I'm sure he didn't bring the magazine deliberately to show me. He didn't have to.'

'You knew?'

'Of course I did. There are ways of knowing you wouldn't understand. You can't possibly imagine how humiliating it is for your husband to make love to you while wishing you were someone else. And then she's the one who becomes rich and famous and has the world at her feet. That's what they are saying in the magazine. Everyone adores her. I'm the one who did nothing wrong and I'm stuck here, with just a miserly allowance.'

Rachel looked again at the photograph of the elegant woman being hailed as the next great star of the moving pictures. It was clear Giselle Harding had bloomed into an even more striking beauty than the determined young actress Aunt Flora had once taken such pleasure in belittling. There might, if you looked closely, be steel in the eyes, but it was carefully hidden with feminine softness.

She could never say so to Louisa, but Rachel envied Miss Harding's resolve to overcome the loss of Peter and make a success of her life on her own terms. She wished she could find the same strength in herself.

'I'm sorry,' she said quietly. 'But marrying Tobias isn't going to solve that. The Howells must have all been well aware that Peter had a mistress he would never give up. What else might they not be telling you?'

'You didn't tell me, either.'

'I was too afraid to try. Don't you see? That's exactly why I'm saying something now. I don't want to repeat my mistake.'

'Well, I'm still going to marry him,' said Louisa sullenly. 'I'm not going to spend my time in a backwater like this, or being nice to a horrible old woman like Aunt Julia. Besides, I'd look like a fool if I changed my mind. And there's nothing you can say that can stop me.'

Chapter Nineteen

It was early morning when Jess stopped in front of Enys Hall.

Close up, it didn't seem nearly so grand as she remembered it as a child, or as it appeared from the harbour. Here, she could see the peel of paint and the grubbiness of many of the upstairs windows that were clearly no longer in use.

Dad said there used to be scores of servants working there when he was a boy. That had always been the tradition. The men worked on the trading ships or the harbour, the young girls worked at Enys Hall, along with the men and boys not suited to going to sea, while the married women took in the family's mending and washing. Miss Hill, the seamstress who had first taught Aunt Sara, had trained up the more promising girls in the art of creating the latest fashions from Paris with only artists' sketches in the magazines to work from.

Jess could just about remember when the candlemakers in the harbour had done a roaring trade. She had loved the smell of freshly cut wood in the workshop where Mr Philips the cabinetmaker had created anything the Bellamy family had needed from the finest of wood. He and his boys had mended anything in the Hall that required their attention and turned anything discarded into something usable for one of the families in the village, or for the church hall. That was the time the Wilkeses' forge had been kept busy with the horses for the farms and the family's carriage, between creating ornate gates and railings to keep the sheep out of the Hall's gardens.

The money earned from the services to the family had supported a thriving little bakery, next door to a greengrocer's and a butcher. But that was all gone now, the final remnants swept away by the war and the raising of the rents. The harbour was lucky; most of the men had returned from the fighting, but the prosperity had gone, and with it the work to keep them there.

Besides, the men who had returned had seen enough of mud. They wanted a quiet life, indoors, away from the backbreaking work of the farm and the garden, with little pay and no thanks when you grew too old to work. So many had left to serve in department stores and factories, with the young lads coming up showing few signs of wanting to stay.

Jess took a deep breath. With Aunt Sara having already accepted the post at Barringtons and preparing to be in London by the end of the month, she could no longer put off her own decision any longer.

She pressed the parcel containing the pendant and the clasp thrust deep inside her coat pocket. She had finally completed them late last night, polishing them until they gleamed. Even her self-critical eye could see they were more striking and finely made than her previous attempt. She had learnt the lessons and grown in confidence.

She felt so certain, deep in her bones, that if she could just get them in front of Miss Harding, the star couldn't help but fall in love with them. If nothing else, it was her chance. Her only chance. Now, with Miss Harding's time in England nearly over, she just had to overcome the insurmountable problem of getting them to Annette in time.

'Jess!' It was Rachel who opened the door. 'There's nothing wrong at the harbour or with your father, is there?'

'No, Miss Bellamy.' Jess swallowed. This might be the most foolish thing she had ever done. Aunt Sara would certainly tell her so. 'I heard that Hannah left, straight after her grandmother's funeral. I came to ask if the post of maid had been filled.'

'We haven't advertised yet; it should be in the paper next week. Why, do you have someone in mind?'

'I was hoping you'd consider me.'

'You? I understood you were a seamstress.'

'I'm not afraid of hard work.'

'I don't doubt you, but I know you've so many other skills. You'd be wasted as a maid. I thought your aunt said you'd been offered a post in a fashion house in London?'

'I'd rather stay in Cornwall, and I can't abandon Dad.'

'I see.' Rachel scrutinised her closely. Jess saw a touch of sadness cross her face, hastily dispelled. 'The work here is exhausting. I help when I can, but it's still backbreaking, and to be honest, there's no saying how long it might last.'

'I'd still take my chance.'

'Mama would be relieved – are you quite certain?'

'Completely. I can start straight away. Now, if you like. Only…'

'Yes?'

Jess shut her eyes and swallowed her pride. 'Only, if you employ me, could I have an advance on my wages, please? Not much,' she added hastily. She took out the parcel. 'Just enough to send this to London.'

'To London? Isn't that where your aunt is to be employed?'

'Yes. But I can't ask her to take this. Anyhow, it would be too late. I need to get it there for tomorrow. And I can't ask Ben, he's done so much already.'

'Ben?'

'He let me use his workshop. In return for helping him

to try to get his hands to work again,' she added hastily. 'It wasn't for any commercial use.'

'Yes, of course.' Rachel sounded distracted. 'I understand that. I'll make sure my mother does too, if the question ever comes up.' She shook herself slightly. 'May I see?'

Well, if the enamelled hair clasp wasn't commercial, she didn't know what was. But she had to trust someone, or there was no point. Jess unwrapped the little parcel.

'It was a trial piece,' she said anxiously. 'It was just me taking a chance. I promise I won't use Ben's workshop ever again.'

'That's lovely.' Rachel turned the silver clasp around in her hands. 'It's exquisite. I had no idea you were capable of creating something so delicate. And that blue in the enamelling is so rich. My sister would die to own something like this.'

'I'm not expecting you to buy it, it's to show someone in London.'

'I see. So that's why you need to get it there so urgently?'

Jess nodded. 'Tomorrow is the last day I can put it in front of someone who might buy it. She's the kind of woman other women will follow, if that makes sense. It's a chance to get orders for more.'

'Then you can't send something that precious by post!'

'I have to risk it.' Jess blushed. 'I can't ask for enough for the railway ticket. I might never be able to pay it back.'

Rachel turned the pendant in her hand, with its matching image of the sailing boat, this time in a clear blue sea with cliffs of lavender and magenta vanishing into the distance. 'Is this how you wish to make your living?'

'Yes. If I can. I know it will take time, and it may not work, and I'll need to be able to support myself while I begin. But, yes.'

'My father always said the forge was as much at the centre of the harbour as the shipping.'

Rachel swallowed hard. She knew instantly this was exactly what Ben needed. She had seen him walk with a lighter step over the past days, as if he had finally found some hope for the future. She might have known it was down to Jess Morgan and her breathtaking skills with metal and enamel. If she could do her best to secure a future for the harbour, she could do the same for the little workshop behind the forge.

Pain shot through her, followed by an agony of despair. She could see them in her mind's eye, the way it was always intended to be. Ben and Jess working in close proximity, sharing a passion for a skill she could never in her wildest dreams possess. Setting up a business together, which would inevitably lead to marriage and a family. She'd seen it happen so often in the harbour. Even when love came later, she'd seen the strongest of bonds being created between those working together to ensure a business survived. Every last inch of her body rebelled against the thought. But she owed Ben that chance at happiness.

'If the harbour's to thrive again, this is exactly the kind of business it needs,' she said firmly. 'Just as much as it needed employment for local girls from your aunt's sewing enterprise, which will be sadly missed. London has money – we need some of it to find its way down here.' She took a deep breath, swallowing every last morsel of her pride. 'Very well, I'll inform Mama there's no need to advertise for a maid – we have found one. And that she is commencing her duties by chaperoning me on a visit to London.'

'Miss?'

'You want to make sure this gets there, and in time, don't you? It's probably best if I don't tell Mama. I'll drop hints about meeting up with an old admirer. I'm afraid she'll agree to anything if she thinks I've come to my senses and I'm finally pursuing a husband. Two tickets to London will seem a small price to pay. We should start as soon as possible. I'll make sure a message gets to your father to say you are safe and you are working here from now on. Come on, there's no time like the present.'

Once she had made up her mind to something, Rachel was a whirlwind. Mrs Bellamy was slightly startled at this sudden turn of events, but had learnt that it was pointless to stand in her daughter's way when she was in this determined mood. Not to mention holding out hope that the vague hint of romance lay at the bottom of her sudden enthusiasm.

While Mrs Bellamy promised to go in person to speak to Dad and Aunt Sara, Jess found herself encased in one of Rachel's coats, along with a pair of Louisa's boots, without any possibility of protest.

'She won't notice. She hardly wears them,' said Rachel, reaching for a hat to complete the outfit. 'Besides, once we've gone, there's nothing she can do about it. There you go, Jess. You don't look at all the part of a lady's maid, but that won't matter once we get away from here. You look exactly as you are: a skilled craftswoman. Come on. Tobias will be bringing Louisa back from St Ives in an hour or so – the last thing I want is to meet them on the way. Time to get going.'

The moment they arrived in London, Rachel hailed a cab, with an imperious wave of the hand that had the first one screeching to a halt at their feet. Jess could have laughed remembering her own timidity at trying to catch a driver's attention when she had been here last time, in her dowdy and soot-stained clothing.

Rachel's coat might not have been of the latest fashion, but, like the one she was wearing, it was unmistakably of the highest quality. This time when they arrived in Barringtons, they were ushered straight into Mr Simms' office without question.

Jess had never been so glad to find Mr Simms was again on the other side of town and that it was Mr Edwards who joined them, slightly bemused at their sudden appearance.

'Miss Fairbairn? I'm sorry, Miss Morgan, I'm afraid she's not here today.'

Jess bit down her disappointment and a faint twinge of panic. 'Do you know where she is?'

'I'm not entirely sure. I believe she was meeting a friend from America. She mentioned the British Museum.'

Relief went through Jess, followed instantly by fear that she might be too late, after all. 'Will she be back here today?'

'I'm afraid not. She asked for the whole day off. Her friend is due to travel to Southampton tomorrow to catch the liner back to New York.'

Jess looked at him in despair. 'How far is it to the British Museum?'

'It's all right,' said Rachel. 'It's easy by cab, I've been there plenty of times before the war. Let's hope we can catch them before they leave. Although the place is vast, as I remember it.'

'Miss Fairbairn said they were particularly interested in the Egyptian antiquities, if that helps,' said Mr Edwards. 'Something to do with her friend being in films and researching her next role, I believe.'

'Thank you,' said Jess, as they set off back through the department store, heading hastily down to the street.

Rachel quickly hailed a cab that took them between motor

vehicles and motorised buses until they alighted in front of the steps and pillars of the British Museum. Jess followed her between cases of artefacts, senses reeling, her hand instinctively diving into her pocket towards her notebook. But she hurried on until they came within sight of two women pausing to admire a severe-looking Egyptian statue that towered above the rest.

'That's them!' exclaimed Jess, racing towards them, ignoring the disapproving stares at a young lady displaying so little decorum.

'Jess!' Annette turned as she reached them. 'You came. I knew you wouldn't let me down.'

'I'm so sorry I couldn't bring the clasp earlier, Annette – it took me longer than I thought. Mr Edwards told us you were here.' She glanced quickly at the woman next to her, face obscured by the veil of her hat. 'I thought I was going to have to send the clasp and pendant by post.'

'You've brought them?'

'Yes. Miss Bellamy kindly came with me...' Jess turned round to find Rachel had made no attempt to move any closer.

'Giselle,' Annette was saying, 'this is Miss Morgan from Cornwall, who made the hair clasp you were so interested in. It seems you'll be able to see it, after all.'

'Pleased to meet you, miss,' murmured Jess, feeling overwhelmingly shy. She had never met a woman who appeared in moving pictures all over the world and who was famous enough to have her photograph in newspapers and magazines. She wasn't quite sure what to say next. But the actress was unaware of her very existence. She was staring past her to where Rachel had remained stock-still by the statue.

'Giselle?' Annette touched her companion's arm. 'Giselle, what is it?'

'I can't stay here.' With that, Miss Harding turned on her heel to disappear between the statues, white veil streaming out behind her.

Chapter Twenty

'I'm so sorry, Jess,' said Annette, returning from a fruitless search. 'I can't think where Miss Harding can be. She may well have returned to her hotel. This is so unlike her. I can't believe she could do this, especially when she had been so eager to see your work. Hollywood must have changed her more than I thought.'

'Don't blame Miss Harding,' said Rachel. 'This is my fault. I'm sorry, Jess. I can't blame her for not wanting to be anywhere near me.' She turned to Annette. 'You have to believe me – I'd never have come with Jess if I'd known. The last thing I want is to embarrass Miss Harding. I know all about the rumours in the newspapers. My sister Louisa was married to Peter Howells, you see.'

'Oh.' Annette digested this.

'But you can't blame Jess. She knew nothing about it. And you have to at least look at the hair clasp.'

'Of course.' Annette smiled. 'I'm sorry about Miss Harding, but I can't possibly let you come all this way without seeing what you've done, Jess. I was so hoping you'd manage to finish something for me.'

She led the way to an empty seat next to the statue, where Jess brought out the box containing the pendant and the hair clasp and unwrapped them carefully, her mind in a whirl. There had been rumours in the harbour of Peter Howells keeping an actress stashed away out of sight, but the shameless, forward creature, no better than she should be and out for what she could, get bore no resemblance at all to Giselle Harding. No wonder she hadn't stayed to see her work. Jess had seen enough of newspapers and gossip magazines obsessed with the love stories of stars from the moving pictures to understand why Miss Harding wouldn't want anything that could even remotely be connected with Peter Howells. However beautiful her work, Miss Harding was hardly likely to buy it now.

As she freed the enamelled clasp, Annette seized on it eagerly.

'This is beautiful, Jess. Even more than the one in the photograph. That design is so atmospheric, and the colours are so vibrant. If I was ready to open my emporium, I would take them straight away. Miss Harding has agreed to be my backer, but the building needs renovation and it will take me months before I can open its door. I can't ask you to keep them for me for that long. There might be somewhere else that would take them.' She sighed. 'I know you have to earn a living straight away, Jess. I heard what happened with your aunt and that you've been offered a post at Barringtons as well.'

'Yes. I haven't replied yet.' Jess looked down at the clasp. She had been concentrating so much on completing it to the best of her ability, she hadn't realised just how much hope she had let ride on one small thing. Maybe all it had ever been was a way to put off the inevitable and face the fact that she would never be able to make a living from her own work.

'The post you were offered was at Barringtons?' Rachel frowned at her. 'But that would give you more of a chance of being independent. You can't be a maid, Jess, and especially not at Enys Hall. It's such a monstrosity it would take all your energies – you'd never be able to do anything else. If you took a post with Barringtons, at least you'd know your evenings would be free and you could find somewhere you could set up.'

'Yes,' said Jess, trying to hide a wave of despair. Rachel was doing her best, but even she didn't understand the financial reality of low-paid work, always much less for women than that commanded by a man who, the logic went, had a family to support. Even now, when so many women were the sole breadwinners for fatherless children, or men too injured mentally and physically by the war to ever work again.

She had tried so hard, but if she came to London, she had a feeling she would never be able to afford to rent even the smallest workshop to do her work; and without work to sell, how could she attract more work and commissions? Besides, Aunt Sara had it all planned out: they would share the rent of a house and bring Dad with them, so he could have a roof over his head in his old age.

Since Sara had been offered a higher-paid position than a mere seamstress, Jess could feel in her bones she would have even less time to herself than she had in the harbour, taking care of the house and making sure Dad was happy when he had fewer interests to occupy him. How was she ever to find a place to work, let alone the time to make anything? Her friends and her whole life were in St Ives and the harbour.

Besides, crept the whisper into her heart, if she came to live in London she would never see Frank again.

'Don't look so despairing, Miss Morgan. I'd say you should definitely never become a maid.' Jess turned to find Miss Harding at her elbow, veil pushed back, gazing down at the enamelled clasp. 'Not if this is an example of your work. Annette was right – it's beautiful and very unusual.' She turned towards Rachel, meeting her eyes square on. 'Miss Bellamy. I believe we have met before.'

'Yes, I remember.'

'At Barringtons, as I recall. When I was working as a mannequin to support myself.'

'I'm not my aunt,' replied Rachel, blushing furiously. 'Believe me, Miss Harding, I didn't support anything she did that day.'

'Yet you said nothing.'

'What was I supposed to say? In my defence, I was young and inexperienced. Aunt Flora assumed it would all go over my head. I didn't fully understand her actions until it was too late.'

'You will forgive me if I struggle to believe you, but how can I, when your sister is about to marry another Howells?'

'How did you know that?' demanded Rachel. There was a moment's silence. 'Of course. How stupid of me. He told you.'

'Tobias is a man who likes to win and to have the power to hurt others. I rather think he came to London purely for the pleasure of informing me in person. And to crow that the harbour was about to be turned over entirely to his control.'

'Not if I have anything to do with it!' exclaimed Rachel. 'He might have gained influence over my sister and some over my mother, but I won't let him turn the harbour into a warehouse or a munitions factory. I want more artists to come and use it, and for businesses like Jess's to thrive there.' She frowned. 'But why on earth would he think the harbour might be of any interest to you?'

'It doesn't matter now. It's in the past.'

'I think maybe we should find tearooms,' broke in Annette. 'Jess and Miss Bellamy have come all the way from Cornwall – they must be exhausted.'

'Yes, of course. I would like to hear more about your work, Miss Morgan, and I am most definitely interested in your hair clasp. I would like to hear more of your ideas. I take it you're staying with your aunt, Miss Bellamy?'

'Certainly not! She's no idea I'm in London and I don't want her to know. I shall find a hotel for me and Jess.'

'There's no need for that,' said Annette. 'You are welcome to stay in my apartment. Vera will be pleased to see you again, Jess, and my bedroom is empty. I'm staying in the same hotel as Miss Harding while she's in London, so we can finalise our plans for my emporium.'

'It's a question of privacy,' said Giselle. 'I'm afraid I tend to become the centre of attention, even when I'm here in a private capacity, and I've no wish for my private business to become the subject of gossip. The Savoy is very discreet.' A look of determination came over her face. 'So that is where we shall go. All of us. Miss Bellamy and Miss Morgan shall also be my guests. I am a very good customer, so I'm certain they will be able to find rooms for you both. As my guests, naturally.'

'For Jess,' said Rachel. 'But not for me. I couldn't possibly accept.'

A gleam appeared in Giselle's eyes. 'My dear Miss Bellamy, you must allow me to patronise you. Just this once. That's all the apology I need.'

Rachel laughed, the unexpected sound echoing around the po-faced statues and the serious visitors. 'Very well, Miss Harding. I can see I'll just have to prove I can endure it.'

'Excellent.' Giselle gave a faint smile. 'I'm glad I returned, in more ways than one. Now, if you'll come with me, I've a cab waiting.'

Giselle was right. Once they reached the grandeur of the Savoy Hotel, Jess and Rachel were quickly found accommodation in rooms adjacent to her suite.

'I hope you will join me and Annette this evening,' Miss Harding remarked. 'I prefer to eat in privacy rather than brave the dining room; it is so much more relaxing and I'd rather not have members of the press finding their way in, even here, trying to overhear my every conversation in the hope of finding yet another nonexistent scandal.'

The rooms were large, resplendent with carpets and comfortable chairs, with swathes of curtain at the windows and the largest beds Jess had ever seen.

'Well, I haven't stayed in anywhere so magnificent since I was little,' said Rachel, inspecting the workings of the interlocking doors. 'I'm not sure Enys Hall could ever rise to such luxury.'

'But it has a far finer view,' replied Jess, with a smile.

'That's true.' Rachel brightened. 'And the air, too. I'd quite forgotten London smells.'

When they made their way to join the others, Jess was surprised to find Giselle no longer in her finery, but in a plain linen dress of dusky green, fair hair caught at the back of her neck by an ornate tortoiseshell clasp, its length falling to her waist.

'This is much better,' she said. 'Come on in, Jess. Now I can have a proper look at your work. I was in earnest when I told Annette I was eager to invest in her emporium in order to promote female craft workers and designers. It isn't just that I understand the difficulties of getting your work taken seriously, or noticed at all, if you are a woman. I've seen enough of the world to know that I need to plan for my own future.' She indicated the luxury around her. 'I'm well aware the day will come when I'm too old to play young heroines, and that is all directors are interested in. They see no point in older women, which is ridiculous as we all become more interesting as we grow older. I have an ambition to direct films, but I'm fully aware that may never happen. So I need to invest my earnings wisely.' A slightly mischievous smile lightened the accustomed seriousness of her face. 'With some extravagance, of course. I've worked too hard and lived with too little not to enjoy a touch of luxury. I've no particular taste for diamonds or haute couture. But I adore good design and I love everything about your work, Jess.'

'See, I told you,' said Annette, appearing from one of the bedrooms. 'And if Giselle wears them, especially the hair clasp, that will be the best advertisement you could get. I would love to stock your work, Jess. Giselle has promised to come over for the opening. So it would be good publicity for all of us if I could display more of your work when I open.'

Jess straightened her shoulders. She was, after all, being given a chance, of the kind that most definitely would never come again. 'I'll find a place to work. But not here. I won't be able to complete anything if I take the post in London. I know my aunt is trying to do what she thinks is best for me, but that means being safe and working as a seamstress for the rest of my life. She can be very forceful, especially if my dad comes too.' She took a deep breath. 'Besides, I want to stay in the harbour. I don't mean I never want to visit London, or plenty of other places, if I ever have the means. But the harbour is where my heart is. I loved gaining ideas about the different styles I could work with while I was here, but it's the Cornish landscape and the sea that has always been my inspiration.'

'I can understand that,' said Giselle quietly.

'And it's more than that. I love the energy here, even more than last time, and the energy in St Ives. But what I learnt over these past days when I was finishing the clasp was that I work at my best in the calm of the harbour.' She hesitated, struggling to put the feeling into words, as much for herself as her companions. 'I suppose you could say it's where my soul is set free. I'm not sure I could find that anywhere else.'

'That's how I feel the moment I step onto a stage or before a movie camera,' said Giselle. 'Whatever else might be happening in my life, it's those moments that make the world make sense. I'm not sure I could live without that, either.'

'Well, in that case we can work something out so Jess can work in the harbour,' said Rachel. She squared her shoulders. 'I'll sure Ben will continue to let you have use of the workshop, Jess. Especially when he knows this is a chance to make a living from your work.'

'I don't want to cause trouble.'

'Trouble? What trouble?' Rachel came to a halt. 'Don't tell me. Tobias.'

'Tobias?' said Giselle sharply.

'It's nothing,' said Jess. She bit her lip, everything she had ever had drilled into her about knowing her place, and not interfering with her social superiors, wrestling inside. On the other hand, her niggling unease would not let go. 'I may have caused Ben enough trouble already. Mr Tobias heard that the workshop was being used when I was making these. He sent one of his men to see us. If he persuades Mrs Bellamy to put up the rent on the workshop, like he has on the other businesses, Ben and his family will have to leave, too.'

'That is why the businesses are leaving the harbour?' said Rachel slowly. 'Jess, are you telling me that Tobias is deliberately forcing them out?'

Jess nodded miserably. 'Yes, miss.'

'And is that the reason your aunt took the premises in St Ives to build up her sewing business and is now giving it up to take the post at Barringtons?'

'Aunt Sara could have afforded the rents in the harbour once she was given the commission from Barringtons, but she kept on being told there was nothing available to rent, even though most of the buildings are lying empty.'

'I should have known,' said Rachel. 'I had a feeling he was up to something, being so solicitous about helping Mama, telling her that it had been Peter's final wish that he made sure the harbour was safe.'

'Is that what he's saying?' Giselle's eyes filled with tears. 'Peter was a fool.' She pushed back her chair. 'Excuse me, I need some air.' With that, she disappeared behind the curtains at the far side of the room, which swayed in the night breeze as she pulled open the door to the small balcony.

Rachel turned back to Jess. 'You don't really think Tobias might harm Ben, surely?'

'I'm don't know. But Ben's certain he'll find an excuse to put up the rent so they can't afford to stay.'

'My mother said she had agreed with the increase to cover the maintenance, that was all. She assured me Tobias suggested a figure that was affordable, but more in line with similar workshops in the area.'

'It's far more than that, miss. It's higher than the rents in St Ives, or Penzance, and Mr Howells has already been telling the ones that are left they will be raised again next year. Ben and his family are struggling to keep afloat as it is. Morwenna can't work any more hours than she is already.'

'I should have known. No wonder he didn't like it when I suggested lowering them again to make sure the workshops were filled. I'll speak to my mother as soon as we get back and make sure she gets proper advice.'

'It not just that,' sighed Jess. 'I expect I could find somewhere else to set up for a short time, but having me there working on these at least got Ben back into the workshop. He's trying so hard. I know he might not ever be able to work as he did before, but he's been a changed person since he began to to find ways of working. It feels like he's coming back to life.'

'I see,' said Rachel. A strange expression passed over her face, almost immediately vanishing. 'Don't worry, Jess. I'll do everything I can to prevent the Wilkeses from having to leave, if it's the last thing I do.'

'That sounds like the dinner service arriving,' said Annette, as the clattering of dishes sounded outside the door. 'I'll let Miss Harding know.'

'I'll go,' said Rachel, making her way towards the balcony.

Chapter Twenty-One

'It's beautiful, don't you think, looking down on the city,' Giselle remarked as Rachel joined her on the balcony.

'Very.'

'I like to see the rush down there, while remaining calm and able to think, out of sight, without anyone knowing I'm here.'

'I don't want my family to cause you any trouble, Giselle. I hope things don't become difficult for you when my sister marries Tobias.'

'No more than they are already.' Her face was turned away. 'Perhaps I should not have brought you here. You or Miss Morgan.'

'But you can't turn down Jess's work because of me or my family connections. That wouldn't be fair.'

'It's not as simple as that. I'm not sure you'd want me to have anything to do with Jess's work, or the harbour.'

'The harbour?'

There was a moment's silence. 'You might as well know. Tobias won't be able to keep his triumph a secret for ever, that's not his style. Peter was always so determined to see the best in everyone. Before he left for France that last time, he asked Tobias to look out for my interests should he not return. I don't expect it ever crossed his mind he was also giving him the power to harm me.'

'Harm you?'

'Peter left me a share of the harbour.'

Rachel stared at her. 'You own part of the harbour?'

'Not exactly. Peter wanted me to have the land on the side where the Howells planned to build warehouses. Peter told me his father insisted he bought it from your family when they were desperate for money, just before his marriage to Louisa. He left it to me.'

'I don't understand.'

'Peter said he wanted to make sure I had something. I'd already told him I didn't need anything from him and especially not money or jewels. That would have made me feel unbearably cheap, as if all I had ever loved him for was his money. I never thought he'd leave me a piece of land. To be perfectly honest, I think he felt guilty that he hadn't stood up to his father's wishes and refused to marry your sister. Maybe he thought that would make it right. He wasn't quite himself that last time I saw him, when he was on his way back to join his regiment. I don't mean that he was a coward, or that his mind had gone. Just that the overload of horrors would not let him go.'

'I know what you mean.'

'Yes, of course. I forgot you had been out there.' Giselle turned towards her, tears in her eyes. 'Peter said you were fearless when it came to looking after those poor refugees who'd been rescued from a shipwreck, and you've seen so much since. You, of all people, must know what I mean.'

'He seemed perfectly rational when I last spoke to him.'

'Oh, he was. In some ways his mind was clearer than I'd ever known it. He didn't say so to me, but I think he knew in his heart he would not survive. From the little he told me, I don't know how any of them survived.'

'No,' said Rachel, shuddering. 'Even the things I saw left me a little mad, and that was nothing compared to some.'

'I think it was his way of trying to make things right.'

'I know he married Louisa to increase his family's influence over the harbour, if that's what you mean.'

'He should have married you.'

'*Me?*'

'I told him so at the time. He had a great deal of respect for you, you know.'

'That's not love.'

'But it might have become so.'

'Never! I could never love a man who was marrying me for convenience, especially to cement his family's future prosperity. I'd rather die in a ditch.'

'Easily said.'

'I mean it,' said Rachel fiercely. 'I'd rather live my life on my own than a lifetime of loneliness in a house in which I was surrounded by others. I'd rather lose love than never have known it at all.'

Giselle eyed her closely. 'It seems we are more alike than I thought.'

'Maybe we are. Although I'm not sure I like the idea of you marrying me off without any consideration for my feelings on the subject,' she added tartly.

'I have to confess I wasn't considering them at the time. Love makes you selfish, but youth is also full of grand gestures. I thought Peter would have more chance of happiness with you than Louisa. Of leaving me behind.'

'If you are saying my sister has a tendency to be a little vain and self-absorbed, I'm not going to argue. But she is a human being, with a right to respect and happiness.'

'As I said, love is selfish. I'm not proud of myself. In the end, I didn't fight him. I suppose, in my heart, I knew if he married your sister, he would always come back to me. I can be perfectly ruthless you know. How else do you think

I got to where I am? And there's no need to look at me like that. I've been punished well enough. Tobias has been my punishment.'

'Tobias?'

'I loved Peter with all my heart, but that doesn't mean I didn't recognise his faults. Maybe that was why I never completely trusted him. I always knew he would betray me in the end. He didn't mean to, he never would. Until that last time, I'm not sure he even saw marrying your sister as any barrier to our life carrying on as it was before. Plenty of men of his class marry for convenience or find they have no choice. He never saw how it would be looking through my eyes. He never did quite understand why I wanted us to never meet once he was married. And he never consulted me about asking Tobias to look after my interests.'

'Which we both know he would never do.'

'Quite. I'd never even have known about the harbour if Peter hadn't asked his sergeant to post a letter to me if he was killed out there. I didn't want anything from the Howellses. I would never have challenged them. But I was so ill after Peter died, I couldn't work. You have to believe I did truly love him, despite everything. How can you pour your soul out on stage and grieve over losing everything when you have no soul left? By the time I wrote to the Howellses, I was desperate for money, my savings had gone, I could no longer keep a roof over my head and I was terrified I would end up on the streets, selling myself to survive. I should have known that trying to fight Peter's family was the last thing I should have done.'

'But they couldn't refuse, surely, not if it was in his will? There must be some legal safeguard.'

'I had no money to pay a lawyer to assert any rights I might have. Tobias was prepared. He said that if I persisted in trying to take advantage of the family's grief, as he put it, he had a dozen men who would testify that they had paid for my "services" and I was nothing more than a common prostitute. I was an actress who had lived for years with a man who was not her husband. He knew how easily any stories of my moral turpitude would have been believed. Tobias could pay for it to be put in the papers. As it was, he did his best to make sure that I would never find work again.'

'But you did.'

'Not for a while,' she said slowly. 'Theatre after theatre refused to hire me. I didn't need to guess why. That's the irony, of course. Tobias won, as he knew he would. I finally had to give up on my dream. I was desperate enough to answer an advertisement for a clerk in a small company making moving pictures. The man who interviewed me for the post had seen me play Cordelia in *King Lear*. They were looking for a tragic heroine and I fitted the role to perfection. When that was a modest success, he offered me the lead part in his next film. When the company suggested I go with them to America, it felt like an answer to my prayers. I never dreamed how much of an answer, or that it would lead to all this.'

'So Tobias drove you away and kept the land.'

'Except that now, of course, I have more than enough means to hire a lawyer, the best lawyer money can buy, should I chose.'

'Then you should! If Peter intended you to have that land, it's yours.'

'It has crossed my mind, especially tonight. I could make sure Jess has a workshop there, and I could invest in the other businesses. The last time I saw him, Peter had changed his mind about his father's plans for eventually buying out the Bellamys. He said he wanted to see it thrive, rather than simply become a warehouse for his father's businesses. He told me it was a place for the living, not containers of explosives.'

'Then fight. You can't let Tobias win.'

'Except that with men like Tobias, sometimes allowing them to think they have won is the only way to keep yourself safe. He could still drag my name through the dirt and there are many who would believe it. Who would believe an actress has only had one love in her life, whatever his faults; and, despite his betrayal, has always remained faithful to him and most probably always will? No one. I don't want to risk throwing away everything I've ever worked for.'

'I hate love,' exclaimed Rachel. 'I wish it was rational. It makes life so utterly impossible.'

'Especially when you love where you are not supposed to,' said Giselle. 'Forgive me, but it crossed my mind earlier that it might be true of you, too.'

'Am I that obvious?'

'Not in the least. It was just that there was so much pain in your face. The kind of pain I recognised.'

'You won't say anything?'

'Of course not.' Her eyes were understanding. 'Forgive me for asking, but is it quite impossible?'

'Utterly. It should never have happened. It's completely impossible now.'

'Things were different during the war,' said Giselle, watching her closely.

'But that doesn't make it any easier.' Rachel blew her nose, swallowing down lump of tears in her throat. 'We'd better go. The others will be wondering what's happened to us.'

'Well, it seems to me you have to fight,' remarked Annette, as the four of them settled down to eat. 'This Tobias sounds perfectly vile – you can't possibly let him win.'

'I agree,' said Rachel, 'but I just don't see how. Even if I could persuade my mother, we simply don't have the means to take on the Howellses.'

'You might not have the business, but you do have the house,' remarked Giselle. 'Peter said it was charmingly old-fashioned, like a manor house out of a storybook, and with the most magnificent view. And didn't you say that if your sister marries again she relinquishes her part?'

'That doesn't mean Tobias won't pretend he owns it,' said Rachel gloomily. 'He's a bully of the first order, with scant regard for other people's feelings, let alone anything so inconvenient as the truth.'

'Then if you are going to do anything, you need to act fast, before they are married. If it's the only thing you have – use it.'

'I've considered that,' admitted Rachel. 'I've been trying to persuade my mother that we use the house to provide us with an income. Turn it into a guesthouse for summer visitors.'

'I'm sure you could,' said Jess. 'When I lived in St Ives there were plenty of families who'd lost their source of income in the war who were renting out rooms to artists or holidaymakers.'

'Exactly,' said Giselle.

Annette nodded. 'There must be hundreds of visitors to Cornwall now things are getting back to normal.'

Rachel sighed. 'The trouble is, Enys Hall is falling down around our ears.'

'That sounds romantic to me,' said Giselle, with a smile.

'You haven't seen the state of it.'

'But all you would need would be a room or two to start with. If it's successful, you could invest back into it and build up from there.'

'I can help you get it up and running,' said Jess. 'It's in my interest too if I want to stay in the harbour.'

'And I know plenty of people in London who would love to stay in a guesthouse in Cornwall,' said Annette. 'And Giselle knows even more.'

Rachel looked at the eager faces around her. 'I can't say I ever saw myself spending my life running a guesthouse.'

'But it doesn't have to be for ever,' said Giselle. 'See it as a means to an end.'

'Yes, that's true. If it could give me the freedom to do what I really want and for you to establish your business, Jess, then it would be worth it. Although I'll still need to convince my mother, and Louisa will be horrified. I don't like the idea of driving her even further into Tobias's arms.'

'It seems to me it's too late for that already,' said Giselle gently. 'At least if you and your mother can make a living, Louisa might have a place to come back to, should she ever need it.'

'That's true. And we'd be taking control of our futures, rather than waiting to see what Tobias tries next.'

'Besides,' said Jess, 'Dad is certain some of the old businesses would return if they have some security. That's why he was pleased when he thought Aunt Sara might be moving back.'

'In that case, I'll make you a deal,' said Giselle. 'If the two of you between you can prove you can make this work, and the harbour attracts businesses and Enys Hall becomes a thriving guesthouse, I'll invest in the harbour. I might even make sure Tobias hands over the land Peter left to me. Peter told me that last time that he wanted me to have it because he believed I would benefit the harbour. I thought that was just a romantic gesture at the time. But now I know you both, I feel I'd rather like to try.'

'Well?' Rachel turned to Jess. 'I don't want to drag you into something against your will. Tobias won't dare do much to me, but you and your dad are far more vulnerable, and I'm not sure how much I can protect anyone who stands in his way.'

'It gives the harbour a chance,' said Jess. 'And I can't imagine the harbour without Enys Hall. We should at least try.'

'It will take hard work to get Enys Hall up to scratch. You might not be able to do much of your enamelling for a while.'

'But I can't in any case, until I have a place to sell my work.'

'Which I'm afraid won't be for a few more months,' put in Annette.

'Besides, I don't want Tobias to win,' added Jess.

Rachel smiled. 'I agree. It's time Tobias learnt that you can't push a bunch of women around just because they are women.' She looked around the table with a gleam of determination in her eyes. 'And now he has the four of us to contend with. I'm looking forward to the fight.'

Rachel stayed behind for a while after Jess, who could barely keep her eyes open after spending all hours finishing the hair clasp, crept off to her own room and Annette had also taken her yawns off to bed.

'Are you quite sure about this, Giselle? I have a horrible feeling this could turn nasty. And you have a lot to lose too if it all goes wrong.'

'I shall be safely in America.'

'I mean your reputation. I haven't forgotten what you said about Tobias threatening to drag your name through the mud. I don't believe newspapers respect the barriers of the Atlantic Ocean. If he manages to raise a scandal, I can't see it being confined to London reporters.'

'I'll take my chances. You and Jess are the ones taking the real risks. Promise me you'll get yourself and your mother, and Jess and her father, out of the harbour if things should become too difficult.'

'Yes, of course.'

Giselle filled two brandy glasses, handing one to Rachel. 'Forgive me asking, but what did you mean just now? You seized so eagerly on the idea of turning Enys Hall into a guesthouse as a means to an end, I wondered if you'd decided what that end might be?'

'I'm not sure.'

'No?'

Rachel took an unladylike gulp of her brandy. 'I have to do something with my life. I'm not cut out to be simply a wife and mother and collect for the poor in my spare time. At least when I was in France, horrible though it was, I felt I had a purpose. I hate myself for saying so, but it's the time in my life when I felt most alive.'

'There's no need to feel guilty, I've heard others say the same.'

'I thought I was going mad. I can't get them out of my mind, you see. The men we couldn't save and the women and children we watched die before our eyes, some simply from starvation. Every night when I try to sleep I can feel them there, staring at me.'

'Rachel, you did what you could under the most terrible of circumstances.'

'But not enough. Not nearly enough. It doesn't make any difference, being there, to the ones you can't save. They only have that life. You can't ever bring that back.'

'So now you feel have to do something,' prompted Giselle gently.

'At least that time in France gave me skills. I don't mean

anything like Jess. I don't have a creative bone in my body. But I'm good at organising. I can drive a motorised vehicle of any kind, and I know I can deal with anything that's thrown my way. It's struck me that there are so many women and children here at home who are in desperate straits. At least I could feel I was doing something. Especially for the women and children. The women who have children out of ignorance, or from force, and the children who are abandoned or left to survive dreadful abuses.'

'Oh?'

Rachel coloured at the gentle prompting. 'Not because of what you might think. I don't have an abandoned love-child out in France.'

'I didn't for one moment think you did.'

'But I could have done.' Rachel drained the last of her brandy. 'That's the part that's haunted me, almost as much as the rest. I was one of the lucky ones. I've been horribly aware ever since that it was only luck. I was brought up in so much ignorance about men and sex. Things were different out there, when we might have died at any minute. I never thought of the possible consequences until it was too late. I could so easily have thrown away any choice I might have about my future, or how I might live my life. Is that selfish?'

'Not in the least.' Giselle refilled their glasses. 'I always took the greatest of care when I was with Peter that there would be no child. I'm afraid I was certain that would not keep him with me, and if he abandoned us, our fate would be terrible. Now I have the money to support a child, I fear it may be too late. But I'd rather give an abandoned boy or girl a home than have watched my own flesh and blood being neglected out of necessity, even sent away, so I could pursue the only way I have of keeping a roof over our heads and food in our bellies. Believe me, I've known plenty of women who didn't have that choice. I've too often seen what happened to them and their babies. Most men, I've found, have not the slightest idea of the reality of women's lives, or how impossible it is to look after a child on your own and earn a living. They've never been asked for such a thing to enter their minds. I've never yet met a woman who willingly chose to be a prostitute, but I've seen plenty who had been left with no other choice. Why do you think I'm investing most of what I earn now into businesses that will sustain me in the future? I've seen how quickly all this can go. Once you've lived with the fear of ending up on the streets, it never quite leaves you.'

'You'll never end up on the streets, Giselle. And I wish Peter was here so I could box his ears for being selfish and showing so little consideration for you and Louisa.'

Giselle smiled. 'That put the fire back into you. I'm glad you didn't marry Peter. I'm not sure we could then have been friends.'

'I hope we are.' Rachel bit her lip. 'I've never told anybody any of this.'

'I'm a good listener. It's always been how I create my characters. You could say it's the secret to my success. Not that I betray any details,' she added hastily. 'Besides, I think we each hold each other's secrets.'

'That's true.'

'What will you do if you are successful in giving yourself a choice of how you conduct your life?'

'I'm not sure.'

'Although I suspect you may still have to resolve love, however impossible, one way or the other.'

'Yes,' said Rachel. The unaccustomed brandy had made her head swim, but at the same time stripped away all other considerations, leaving her mind clear. Giselle was right. Love was selfish and she wasn't the kind of woman who could simply sacrifice herself and walk away. Now she had given the means for Ben and Jess to work closely together on a shared passion, she would have given anything to take that back. She pushed the treacherous thought out of her mind. 'You are right. I will have to decide, one way or the other.'

Giselle pressed her hand gently. 'Whatever Peter's faults, or how much I knew I might lose him one day, I have no regrets. However impossible love seems now, if you have a chance, then seize it. There are few enough chances for happiness in this world, and even less to find love. The only thing any of us can do is to take the chance we have, and risk the pain. Far better that, than to live life in the shadows, wondering what might have been.'

Chapter Twenty-Two

'A guesthouse?' Mrs Bellamy stared at Rachel in horror. 'Are you telling me that you think the only way is to turn Enys Hall into a place for paying guests? I thought you'd given up that idea long ago.'

'What else are we going to do, Mama? Rattle around, the two of us, freezing each winter, without any staff to help us, until we have no choice but to sell? At least this way we would have a chance.'

'But having strangers in our home. We could be murdered in our beds.'

'I've thought of that. Why don't we make it exclusively for women? They aren't likely to prey on anyone. I've seen plenty of women artists who come on their own to St Ives, or with a maid, so there must be plenty of women artists who would wish to come without the need of some accompanying aunt, who would welcome a female establishment.'

'Just think of the work involved! My dear, I know how much you helped Hannah over these past years, and now we'll have Jess, but the washing alone ...'

'I'm not afraid of hard work. And if we make this a success, we'll be able to hire more staff. There are still young women in the harbour who need work to support their families. Besides, we have Cook. She's our secret weapon, Mama, if we can persuade her to stay. You can tell she's just itching to go back to more adventurous cooking. When she's cross, she always says she's going to start up her own tea rooms in the harbour with her niece. Well, we can provide excellent meals for guests in the evenings, and why shouldn't we turn the drawing room and the conservatory into an elegant tea room?'

'Good grief, you make it sound like some cheap hotel.'

'I was thinking more of the Savoy. Being there again, when I was in London, it reminded me just how much it seemed like a fairy-tale palace when Papa took us to stay, when Louisa and I were small. We might not be as grand, but between us, we could still make Enys Hall a fairy tale in its own way. Special. With Cook's skills, we could make it the kind of place people recommend to their friends.'

'But if so many others are doing the same, how can we be sure anyone will come to us at all, being out of St Ives? I don't want you to get your hopes up and find it comes to nothing.'

'That's a risk we would have to take. Whatever we do, Mama, you and I are going to have to work for our living. I'd rather take the risk here than wait hand and foot on Aunt Julia and then be fit for nothing but advertising to become a lady's paid companion.'

'It might yet come to that, my dear.'

'But isn't it at least worth the try? Jess can use her skills as a seamstress to bring the furnishings up to an acceptable standard; that's much better than just having her simply as a maid. I'm not afraid to clean and help Cook as much as I can until we can afford to employ someone. Besides, we are not completely destitute. Surely it's better to take the risk and employ someone to mend the roof and the guttering and make the outside look presentable than try and drag out the pennies as much as we can? I've had enough of being held hostage to the Howellses and their ambitions and watching the harbour die in front of us.'

'My dear, we may have no choice when it comes to the Howellses.'

'But it's utterly ridiculous that a successful businesswoman like Sara Catchpole is being forced to take up a post in London for lack of premises, when there are half a dozen shops lying empty in the harbour. She has an excellent business, one that could have offered employment to women in the harbour. It might be too late to keep Mrs Catchpole, but at least we could give Morwenna Wilkes a chance to use her embroidery skills before she is driven to work in London as well. Why shouldn't we give the harbour a chance to thrive again and encourage families to stay, rather than being forced to go to Redruth or Truro, or even out of Cornwall altogether?'

Her mother sat in thought for a while. 'I admit it would be nice to see the harbour thriving once again. I don't like to see it so empty. And I have to confess I don't want to be forced to leave. This has been my home for so long.'

'Then we need to do something. There's still some of Papa's money left. Either we hang on for as long as possible or we can take a risk and use some of it to see if we can make it work.'

'I need to think it over.'

Rachel hesitated. 'Mama, it might also be a way we can let Louisa know she has a choice. So she doesn't have to feel her only option for securing a comfortable life is to marry Tobias; that she could still have a home here with us and give her a chance of finding someone who might truly make her happy.'

'I would hope so,' said Mrs Bellamy, without much conviction.

*

Later that afternoon, Rachel knocked as firmly as she could on the door to the little workshop.

Ben turned in his seat. 'Miss Bellamy!'

'Please don't get up. I told your mother I had brought this to be repaired.' She placed the locket decorated with *cloisonné* forget-me-nots on the bench beside him. 'As you created the new catch, it seemed best to bring it to you to be mended.'

He took it in his good hand. 'I'm sorry it's broken.'

She put her hands in her pockets to hide their shaking. It was one thing meeting up on the cliffs, but another in his own domain, surrounded by the tools of the trade he had described to her with so much passion, the half-finished examples of the work he had been able to do with such skill when he had the use of both hands. Still, there was no going back now.

'It isn't. It was the only way I could think to see you.'

'Oh.' He replaced the locket on the bench with care.

'Don't worry, I'm not staying more than a few minutes. I won't risk embarrassing you or provoking rumours. Heaven knows those start easily enough without any cause.'

'Yes, Miss Bellamy.'

'Ben...' His face was serious, his eyes unfathomable. 'Ben, I can't bear this, being so close, and yet so far apart.'

'Then maybe I should leave the harbour.'

'No! Of course not. That's not what I meant. I was hoping you would forgive me.'

'Forgive you?'

'For all I've taken away from you. I'd give anything to take that day back, for you never to have been caught in that explosion.'

'There's nothing to forgive. It could have been any of us. Besides, you kept your head as the mortars fell; if you hadn't

232

swerved when you did we might have all been killed.' His brows drew together as if in pain. 'If you hadn't swerved, you would most certainly not have survived.'

'Yet I came out with barely a bruise, while you …'

'It doesn't matter, Rachel. Truthfully. And besides, while my scars may be visible, I know you were not left unscathed.'

There was a moment's silence. 'I was praying you would forgive me. I can't just forget, Ben, or walk away. I know things were different out there, but so much has changed since the war. Surely something so precious cannot be lost.'

He turned half away from her, eyes on his bench. 'I fear it might be more thoroughly lost, in the hard light of day,' he replied. 'I'm not sure I'd wish that.'

'But we lived every day in France knowing we could lose each other at any hour. Surely we can take that risk again?'

'With what? It is shameful enough being supported by my mother and sister. I've no intention of bringing such shame on anyone else.'

'I …' She stopped as she met his gaze, her exclamation that such things didn't matter arrested on her lips.

'We always knew it was impossible,' he said quietly, pushing the locket gently towards her. 'I could not bear the thought of having regrets.'

Despair went through her. She had no answer, just a deep emptiness within. She did not dare stay longer.

Rachel ignored the locket, leaving it on the bench beside him. 'I have none. I never will,' she said, fleeing through the door before her tears could blind her.

The following morning, Jess followed Rachel on a tour of inspection of the possibilities of Enys Hall as a guesthouse, from the formal dining room to the drawing room stuffed with ornaments and taxidermied birds and animals arranged in scenes under glass domes, the walls crammed with ornate frames around glum-looking Bellamy ancestors.

Rachel was in a restless mood, moving from one thing to the next with nervous energy. Jess wasn't sure that even Rachel's determination not to pause for a moment could tackle the years of clutter. How even an entire army of maids could keep it all dusted, let alone attend to the grates in each room and beat the yards of carpet, was beyond her.

By the time they returned to the hallway, even Rachel looked a little daunted. 'Funny how you can be so used to something you don't see it properly until you view it through the eyes of someone new. I'd forgotten how big it is. And how totally impractical. I'm even less sure anyone would want to stay in a place in this state. It would be a huge undertaking. Has this made you change your mind, seeing the mess we're in?'

'Not in the least. I like a challenge.'

'I had a feeling you might.' Rachel rolled up her sleeves with a determined air. 'Time to make a start.'

As she left later that day, covered in dust and aching from moving furniture and mopping floors, Jess turned to look back at the crumbling mansion. Dad would be glad she was staying, for all his wish for her to do well. Aunt Sara would be disappointed, perhaps a little hurt, but her mind was already on London and her plans for the future.

It had seemed so easy, sitting in the comfortable luxury of the Savoy. This was only for a while, she reminded herself, until she could get on her feet. She would not allow herself to be trapped there for ever, as she would be if she followed Aunt Sara and become a seamstress for the rest of her life.

All the same, Jess couldn't help the small voice warning her that a seamstress was one better than a maid. Mrs Bellamy might be coming round to the idea of turning Enys Hall into a guesthouse, but there was still no guarantee that the idea would work. She had a nagging doubt that she might have just trapped herself into work she hated after all, with no time or energy left to make her jewellery business work. She might just have made the worst mistake of her life.

That afternoon, as Rachel stood at the drawing-room window watching Jess walk down towards the harbour, her sense of emptiness grew stronger.

'You are sure about all this, Mama?' she said, tearing her eyes away as Jess stopped to chat to Mrs Wilkes on the bench outside the forge, followed almost immediately by Ben limping out to join them. 'You've been very quiet all day. I didn't railroad you into this, did I?'

'Of course not, my dear. We need to be practical and explore every option.'

'With Jess's skills, as well as her energy, I'm sure between us all we could make this a thriving place. Oliver would never have given up without a fight. For all his friendship with Peter, he never wanted the Howells to have too much influence over the harbour. I don't want to see them destroy everything Papa and Grandpapa worked so hard to build. Besides, it's only fair that we do everything we can for the people living in the harbour. Without their skills and hard work, the Bellamys would still be clay miners.'

'Yes, my dear, that is very true. Your father was always very conscious of the fact that we owed so much to the harbour and those who made it thrive.' Mrs Bellamy reached into the writing bureau and brought out paper and a pencil. 'The curtains in the hallway need replacing and the ones in here could do with mending and the hem taking up. We could ask Jess to look at brightening up the sofa and upholstering the armchair that really is quite beyond.'

'There must be old curtains in the attic. They might not be as nice but if they are cut down to fit, they'll do. I found a whole trunk of material up there during the war, when we were desperate for winter coats. All of it lying there forgotten. And then there are whole sets of Grandmama's plates and tea settings. They may be old-fashioned, but we can make that a virtue. A touch of a more elegant past.'

'Yes, I suppose there is that.' Mrs Bellamy brightened, her pencil racing over the paper, making list after list.

Rachel took a deep breath. She needed to be busy, to keep her thoughts at bay. 'We could move some of the things in here into the storeroom.'

'But this is how it has always been!'

'I know, Mama, and I hate the thought of it being changed too. But this is how it was in Grandpapa's time. Tastes have changed when it comes to clutter, and it's too much to dust. Even when we had three housemaids, it was hard to keep on top of it all, and Jess has far too many skills to be wasted on needless dusting. It's not as if we are getting rid of Grandmama's ornaments, just putting them in a safe place for a while.' Her eyes strayed toward the fox in the huge glass dome, staring balefully out of silk greenery with his glassy eyes. 'Although I think the first thing to go is Mr Reynard; he's so moth-eaten the stuffing is starting to come out.'

'I suppose it is rather passé.' Mrs Bellamy gazed around the crammed living room. 'I'd almost forgotten that this is how it was when I came here as a bride. Your papa hated to see anything in here changed; it had such memories of his childhood.'

'Then we don't have to alter a thing.'

'Oh, goodness me, my dear. That's not what I meant, not what I meant at all. You just reminded me, that's all. The truth is, I always hated it. From the moment I first set foot inside the house. I should have got rid of these monstrosities years ago. I'm quite embarrassed to bring anyone in here. It's why I always meet people in the conservatory.' She shook herself. 'This room is a monument to your father's childhood, long before he met me. Something I could never share. So much of the world your papa knew when he was a boy has been swept away. But we can't change the past. All any of us has is what the future might bring.'

'Mama.' Rachel put her arms around her mother, holding her tight.

'It's all right, my dear,' said her mother, gently disentangling herself and blowing her nose. 'There's no point in becoming maudlin. And you are right. At least activity and a sense of purpose can act to keep thoughts at bay. At the very least, turning Enys Hall into a guesthouse will keep us occupied. Although how Louisa is going to see this, I dread to think.'

Or Tobias, thought Rachel. All she could hope was that this was a bridge they might never have to cross.

Chapter Twenty-Three

Jess arrived at Enys Hall the next morning to find it already a hive of activity, with Rachel and Mrs Bellamy deep in removing ancient ornaments and inspecting furniture for the ravages of woodworm and moths. Only Louisa kept to her room, refusing to lift a finger and complaining of a headache.

'Does she hate the idea so very much?' Jess asked Cook, as she was press-ganged into scouring pots before starting the cleaning of the cleared spaces in the main part of the house.

'Oh, it's not that. It's Mr Tobias. He's been packed off to America, to supervise the Howellses' New York store.'

'Then he'll be gone for weeks.' Jess could have danced round the kitchen in relief. It seemed luck was finally on their side.

'Trouble is, he'll be back,' said Cook, gloomily.

But at least they had a bit of breathing space. Jess felt sorry for Louisa, who must be mortified at being so abruptly abandoned, but she hoped from the bottom of her heart Tobias would never return. She couldn't help but feel relieved when Louisa accepted an invitation from Mrs Howells to spend time with the family in London while Tobias was away, with the promise of dances and visits to the theatre and the opera.

'Making sure they can keep an eye on her and she doesn't see sense and marry the first man who asks her,' sniffed Cook.

'At least she's happy, and we don't have to worry about

her reporting our every move back to Tobias,' replied Rachel. 'And you never know, it may backfire and she might fall in love with a duke. If there are any left, that is.'

'Now that would be something,' said Cook, returning to retrieving cake tins and jelly moulds from the depths of cupboards where they had been hidden away in expectation of never being used again.

Over the next weeks, Jess worked all hours helping Rachel – who seemed to have acquired a restless, inexhaustible energy since their return from London – move furniture and pack away endless ornaments into old tea chests, hiding them away in the attics. Mrs Bellamy joined them, to hunt through the boxes and trunks already up there, along with a broken rocking horse and old bedspreads, in search of anything that might prove useful.

'My goodness,' exclaimed Mrs Bellamy, as the main sitting room was emptied down to chairs and sofas and the grand piano, all covered with dustsheets in preparation for painting and wall papering. 'I'd no idea it was so large. Or so light.'

With the rooms cleared, they painted and wallpapered as best they could. Despite her frustration at having no time or energy to start on her enamel work, Jess found herself enjoying making the rooms look fresh and welcoming, followed by the mending of curtains and furnishings. The sofa took a little more working out, but she loved the satisfaction of forcing the horsehair back inside and stitching up the seams, followed by replacing the worn covering.

Mindful of everything she had seen in London, Jess did her best to make the lines as clean and uncluttered as possible, without completely losing the touch of old-fashioned charm. At least it was making her think about design and challenging her to do her best with the meagrest of materials.

Mr Rowe, who had run the stables before the war, and

helped out as handyman and gardener when things were desperate, clucked his tongue over the neglect of the shrubs and Rachel's demand to make the outside of the house look as good as new.

'The wood of those top windows needs replacing for a start, Mr Rowe. The sills are clearly rotting and the window in the guest room doesn't properly close; there's a draught flying through in winter. We'd have guests complaining in no time, let alone the fuel to keep the fire as high as we can make it.'

'I'm not sure.' Mr Rowe coughed. 'Thing is, miss, I'm finding I can't do ladders like I used to, not any more. Me missus is afraid of me falling, see. Bones not as strong as they were.'

'Of course you won't fall.' Rachel frowned at him irritably. 'You've been doing this for years and you haven't yet.'

'Always a first time.'

'Perhaps you could try someone younger for the very high bits,' suggested Jess.

'But how are we going to find one?' said Rachel. 'I've tried in the harbour, but no one is interested and the ones who might be willing to have a go have all left.'

'That's true, Miss Bellamy,' nodded Mr Rowe. 'But I do know of one. There's a lad in St Ives good with his woodwork and prepared to do anything. Supporting his sister, see. Not quite right in the head, poor thing, if you know what I mean. Pity. Pretty little thing, for a Frenchie.'

'Do you mean Charlotte Dupont?' said Jess, frowning.

'Aye, that's the one. Paints pictures like them lady artists. The ones who strip down to their wherewithal.'

'Charlotte doesn't strip down to anything!' exclaimed Jess. 'She sometimes works as an artist's model to help pay for her lessons, but it's all very respectable. Her brother wouldn't let her, otherwise, and he always walks her home. I've seen the studio.' She raised her chin slightly. 'I've modelled there myself.'

The old man's jaw dropped. Jess felt her colour rise. No doubt she'd be a scarlet woman by sundown and the madam of the lowest brothel along the south coast by the end of the week. Not that there were any such things, as far as she knew, but the harbour was always rife with rumours of them, along with smugglers and white slave traders and spies who, being foreigners, wouldn't ever accept the war was over.

'I won't hold that against you,' said Rachel, with what sounded suspiciously like a hastily swallowed laugh. 'But perhaps we could try the young man? Despite him being French.'

'It's Frank, Miss Bellamy,' put in Jess. 'Him and his sister were the ones who stayed in the forge that night of the storm. He has a reputation for being responsible and a hard worker.'

'Frank! Of course. I remember them.' A shadow passed over Rachel's face. 'I should have guessed. The WI ladies told me he was doing well and looking after his sister. I understand she still can't speak, poor thing.'

'She understands, miss. You can see she understands English perfectly when she gets to know you.'

'Poor child. I remember her eyes. Very well, I'll speak to him. We can't have paying guests – especially ones we want to come back year after year – while there's a gale blowing through the place.'

Rachel was as good as her word. A few days later Frank appeared in front of the house, having taken very little persuading.

'You stayed,' he said, as Jess left the beating of carpets on the lawn to join him. 'You did not go to work in London.'

'I'm going to send my enamel work to London, but I'm

going to do that in the workshop behind the forge. Where you stayed that night you arrived.'

'I remember,' he said with a faint smile.

She had so much to say, so much to ask, but already Rachel was brandishing a list. 'I know you're primarily a carpenter, Frank, but there are one or two other jobs Mr Rowe can't manage, which I hope you can tackle.'

'I'll try my best, Miss Bellamy,' Frank replied cheerfully.

'It's going to have to be primarily cosmetic. So as long as it looks tidy and there's nothing obviously broken, the rest will have to wait. If this works, I'm rather afraid our first few months', if not years', earnings are going to be eaten up by repairs. But as long as we just do our best for now.'

'This will make a fine guesthouse,' he said, as Jess brought him out a cup of tea later that day. 'There must be plenty who will prefer a place that is quieter than St Ives.'

'I hope so,' she replied, with a smile. 'Once the house is ready for guests, I'll be going back to my enamel work.'

'Then perhaps you will go to London?'

She shook her head. 'My life is here. I couldn't think of living anywhere else.'

'Good.' He turned to inspect a rotten piece of wood. 'My business, it is growing, so I am looking to buy a motorised van one day soon, when this work is done. It is fast journey, only a matter of minutes, on the road from here to St Ives. I can take you, if you like. Diana asks after you, and Charlotte would like to see you.'

'I'd love to,' she replied. 'Thank you. I miss my friends in St Ives, and all the artists too. Once I have a bit more time when Enys Hall is finished, I'll come back and see you all.'

'I would like that very much,' he replied, returning her smile.

*

Within weeks, Enys Hall was looking less neglected. With wood retrieved from the sheds and a lick of paint, Frank repaired the broken frame and the windowsills and removed the worst of the moss encroaching over the roof. Inside, he mended tables and cabinets and restored the balustrade of the central staircase until it almost looked as good as new.

Jess was glad when the worst of the clearing and cleaning was finally over and she no longer staggered home to then fall asleep with exhaustion the moment she and Dad had eaten.

One evening, after seeing Dad settled in front of the fire with his much-thumbed edition of *Vanity Fair*, Jess slipped away down to the forge.

'Well, now, and there's a sight for sore eyes,' said Mrs Wilkes, who was sitting in the evening sun polishing a newly finished selection of fire pokers.

'I'm sorry I haven't been for so long, Mrs Wilkes.'

'Don't be daft. Everyone knows you've all been working like troopers up there at the Hall. Good to see the old place coming back to life.' Her eyes ran around the harbour. 'And this place too. Made a difference it has, since Mrs Bellamy reduced the rents on the workshops. Not as much as they should be, and not everyone trusts that it'll stay that way, but some are finding their way here.'

'I'm glad, and it's nice to see Dad feeling more settled again.'

'Ben'll be glad to see you.'

'So he's still working.'

'Aye, not as much as when you were here, but still better than nothing. I reckon having you there gave him confidence, as well as the company. You coming back then?'

'Now most of the heavy work at the Hall is done, Rachel is insisting I have two afternoons off to work on the pieces for the new shop in London. It's opening in a few weeks' time; I'd better get going. If you are still sure – I don't want to intrude.'

'You'd never intrude, Jess. You'm family. Might not be blood, but blood don't count for everything. Go on then, Ben'll be glad to see you.'

Ben was sitting deep in thought when Jess reached the half-open door, gazing down at a small locket gleaming in his good hand, as if a world away. Unwilling to intrude, she knocked a little hesitantly.

'Jess!' He started, hand closing instantly, hiding the locket from view.

'Your mum said you were here. But if you are busy...'

'Don't be daft.' He placed the object in his hand deep inside his pocket. 'You know I'll always have time for you, Jess.' He cleared his throat. 'Although I thought by the sound of things, Rachel would be working you to death up at Enys Hall for at least the next month. She can be a demon when she puts her mind to it.'

'I think she's still working herself to death,' replied Jess. 'But it's impossible to stop her and she's determined to give me time to make a start on the enamel work for the shop in London.'

'Good for her.'

The air of sadness still hung around him, as if impossible to shake off. She bit her lip. 'Are you sure you don't mind, Ben, me working here again? Diana has offered me space in her workshop to make the new hair clasps for London. I'll be able to get a lift with Frank when he gets his motorised van, but for now it would mean walking to St Ives and back, and I'm going to need all the time I can spare.'

'And the energy, I imagine,' he said. 'You'll be more than welcome, Jess. It will be good to have company.'

'Thank you. At least I can buy materials now, with the payment Giselle made for the hair clasp and pendant.'

'That's quite a coup, you know,' he said, a little wistfully, 'having your work worn by a star of the moving pictures. I know many established jewellers who'd have given their eyeteeth for such an opportunity. But then they don't have your skill.'

'I had a good teacher. The best, in fact.'

'No one could have taught you your eye for shape and colour, or your flair,' he replied gruffly. 'So, have you decided whether you're going to concentrate on the same design as before, or something different?'

'I thought similar to the one I made for Miss Harding but each one unique.' At least all the cleaning and scrubbing had left her mind free to think things through and to plan; while stopping to talk to Ben most evenings, even for a few minutes, had cleared her mind. 'I thought similar, because that's what people will see if Giselle wears hers, and unique because I'm never going to be able to make hundreds of them at a time, so each one needs to be special. I don't know if it will work, but I can try.'

'It's a good idea. I'm sure it will.'

'I hope so.' Her eyes rested on the bench. 'You've found a way of working.'

'Almost.' He looked at the teapot he had been fashioning. 'I can't do the fine work, like mending the clocks or working on jewellery, but I'm getting better at being left-handed. I might be slow, too slow to making a living from my work, but I may soon be able to teach again, thanks to you.'

'I didn't do anything!'

'You insisted I come back into the workshop and you didn't make any comment or try to help when I did try.

245

I'm not sure I'd have done that otherwise. It's not the same, Mum nagging me.'

'I'm glad you've found a way,' she replied, torn between pleasure and sadness.

Ben shook himself. 'Come on then,' he said, his tone that of the instructor once more. 'Let's see these designs you've been working on.'

Jess didn't need any further prompting. She took out her notebook, placing it on the bench and opening it up at her most recent designs. 'These are some of the ideas I've been working on since I got back from London. I've decided I'm going to keep to scenes of Cornwall. That's what I want to be known for, as well as the quality of my work. It will help keep me unique. I'll do a variation on the boat I made for Giselle, but I've not decided which ones would be the best to form a proper collection.'

'Hmm.' He turned the pages with his good hand, going back and forth between the sketches. 'Quite a few have the sea. The blue you used for Miss Harding's clasp was very effective. You could make that the link between them. Or maybe the cliffs. I like the lines they make in the background. That's very evocative.'

They were still poring over the notebook, discussing which designs might work the best, when there was a knock on the open door. Jess dragged herself away from the practicalities of representing the harbour wall in enamel to find Frank watching them from the doorway.

'Come on in,' she said with a smile. 'You remember Ben.'

'I came to visit the forge again. Mrs Wilkes suggested I come and say hello,' he said hesitantly, as if not sure of his welcome.

'Of course,' said Ben. 'We were just going through Jess's

designs. It's good to see you again, Frank. It seems a long time ago you were first here.'

'Yes, it does,' he replied. Everything about him was uncomfortable and distracted, as if the memories of the night he arrived with Charlotte were too painful to bear. He stayed for a short while to admire the designs they had selected as the best for Jess to make as her first collection for Annette, before excusing himself saying that it was late.

'Come again and see them being made,' said Jess, accompanying him to the door.

'Yes. Thank you,' he said, not quite meeting her eyes. 'I am certain they will be beautiful.'

'And tell Charlotte I will see her as soon as these are finished.'

'She will be pleased,' he said, his smile returning a little. 'I understand how important this is for you, Jess. I know Charlotte will too.'

Then he was gone. A few minutes later, she caught a glimpse of him racing away on his bicycle, back up towards St Ives. A turn in the road and he vanished from sight.

Chapter Twenty-Four

'We've had a request already,' said Rachel the next morning, as Jess arrived at Enys Hall.

'How can we, when we haven't advertised?' exclaimed Mrs Bellamy.

'It's a friend of Annette Fairbairn.' She held out a letter. 'Mrs Fitzpatrick and her daughter are painters of water-colours. She wishes to come for two weeks, along with their maid.'

'But we are not nearly prepared. I shall have to reply and tell her so.'

'But then she might change her mind and not come at all,' said Jess.

'Exactly,' said Rachel. 'Jess is right. Besides, the best room is nearly ready. The rest, as long as it's clean, they can put down to romantic decay.'

'But she's from Belgravia. I'm sure even her maid will look down on us.'

'They may be pleasantly surprised, Mama. I'm sure people in London think we live like savages and rampage naked over the heather when the mood takes us.'

'Rachel!'

'We'd better hurry and get that room fit for a princess,' said Rachel hastily, escaping with Jess before laughter over-came them both. They raced up the stairs to the half-finished room, where they came to a halt just inside the door.

'There's still so much to be done,' said Jess, courage failing her.

'Nothing that can't be finished with hard work,' said Rachel. 'I'm not letting this opportunity slip through our fingers.'

A week later, Rachel and Jess stood nervously as Mrs Fitzpatrick and her entourage arrived with several large trunks, accompanied by easels and paintbrushes and a large photographic camera on a stand.

Mrs Fitzpatrick turned out to be a small, nervy woman, whose slender frame was taut with energy, all ready to be unleashed on the rocks and cliffs of the little cove. Her daughter was tall, and equally slender, but of a slightly calmer disposition.

'Oh my goodness. My dear, have you seen this?' Mrs Fitzpatrick swept in, leaving her daughter and maid to bring in the lighter of their belongings, while the driver bringing them from the railway station wielded their trunks, muttering darkly about London folk. She clapped her hands in delight, eyes shooting around, as if already choosing the subject of her next sketch. 'The cliffs and the harbour. So very charming. Just as I imagined Cornwall to be.' She turned as her daughter arrived. 'And look, dearest, you can see the sea from this window. You shall have this room.'

'Oh, but Mama, you said it is the best.'

'I know how much you love the sea. And besides, you are young, Elinor; you need romance in your life. I shall take the room on the floor below, next to Maggie, which also looked perfectly charming.'

Elinor was still looking uncertain.

'There are also fewer stairs,' Rachel whispered tactfully, as she helped their guest with her easel.

'Of course! How silly of me. I hadn't thought of that. Mama does suffer with her knees, and she so hates to confess to any weakness.'

'In that case, probably best to give in.'

'Thank you.' Elinor smiled, her face coming alight revealing a delicate beauty all of its own. 'Mama can be a bit, well, decided, at times.' She moved to the window. 'But she is right, I do love the sea. We were in Scotland last year, in the Highlands. Mama is a devotee of the novels of Sir Walter Scott, and has a love of the Highlands, and was determined to paint them. It was very beautiful, but very wild and vast. I shall enjoy painting the cliffs and the sea.' A touch of mischief appeared. 'And our maid will be happy. Maggie is generally quite adventurous, but she was terrified by the Highlands, convinced some kilted clansman was about to appear at any moment and carry us off to a fate worse than death. She'll be glad to see this is far more civilised. And the light is quite beautiful.'

Cook excelled herself that evening, commanding Jess and Rachel mercilessly. Despite the scolding and the endless amounts of steam, Jess enjoyed the drama of getting perfect dishes up to the dining room still piping hot and on time, followed by delicate confections of jellies and ice cream.

Much to everyone's relief, the visit was a resounding success. Every morning, their guests sallied forth, Maggie in attendance to carry easels and bags of painting materials to the cliffs above the sea, or to various positions in the grounds, even venturing down to the harbour to sketch the boats. Mrs Fitzpatrick, it turned out, was no idle amateur with expensive equipment and little skill, demanding praise from a maid who dare not say otherwise. Mrs Fitzpatrick had studied under Italian masters, still travelled widely in search of the best tutors, and had trained her daughter in the same discipline.

While Elinor concentrated on detailed illustrations of flowers and birds, and the wildness of the cliffs, Mrs Fitzpatrick's sketches of Enys Hall were embellished with knights and ladies of medieval appearance, the crumbling stonework intertwined with hints of secret love trysts and wistful maidens.

'All sounds a bit daft, if you ask me,' remarked Dad, as Jess returned home one afternoon.

Jess tucked her arm through his. 'She's very rich, Dad, and she has plenty of wealthy friends in London. She's already arranged to come back next spring, this time for a month.'

Dad grinned. 'Maybe not so daft, after all. A woman with taste.' He frowned at her. 'But a lot of work for you.'

'I don't mind, Dad. I told you, I like mending furniture and replacing curtains, and at least cleaning leaves my mind clear. I might not have been able to work much on my hair clasps this week, but I'll be able to start again once these guests have gone. Besides, I like spending time with you.'

'You don't have to worry about me, sweetheart. You have your life ahead of you. I want you to be happy, with a family of your own. I don't want you stuck here working as a maid when you could be living the high life in London with Sara.'

'But I like it here. And I'm not just a maid. And I am serious about making my living from my enamel work. It's what I've always wanted to do.'

'So I see.' Dad turned to where Ben was sitting outside in the warmth of the sun, a cup of tea in his good hand. 'I'm glad to have you back in the harbour, and you always were happy in the forge, from when you were a little girl. It's good to see you there again.' A look of satisfaction came over his face. 'Now things are more settled again, I'm hoping you'll always see the harbour as your home.'

*

Over the summer, there was a small but steady stream of visitors to Enys Hall. By the time September arrived, Cook's innovation of providing afternoon tea in the garden in fine weather and in the conservatory when rainclouds threatened had proved a resounding success with walking parties and visiting artists alike.

'Seems I was right to start get the harbour spruced up,' said Dad one sunny afternoon as Jess returned home from serving tea and Cook's delicious cakes. 'For all people's grumbling.'

'It looks as inviting as could be,' smiled Jess. Sure enough, the walkers directed down by Cook to explore the harbour were wandering about in the warm afternoon sun, gushing over the picturesqueness of the place. A photographer had set up his camera to take the fishing boats waiting for the tide. Several of the visitors appeared to have entirely abandoned the idea of a strenuous day tramping the cliffs and were sitting in the sun while a few of the more adventurous were choosing to return by boat.

'Frank did a fine job of repairing the doors and the window frames and once everyone got the idea, they soon mucked in. I'm glad Mrs Bellamy came to her senses and reduced the rents right down. Nice to see the harbour being used again.'

With Louisa still in London and Tobias remaining in New York, the harbour had relaxed. Uncertainty still hanging over the future meant that not all of the old businesses had returned, but several of the workshops on the front had been hired by painters happy to escape the more crowded streets of St Ives.

Morwenna had been the first to take over one of the small shops facing the quay, joining forces with a seamstress offering dressmaking, along with suits and coats, at a reasonable price, which allowed Morwenna to concentrate on her embroidery.

Already a quiet industriousness had returned to the harbour. Jess sighed wistfully. On the road from St Ives, a motor car made its way to Enys Hall: the next guests arriving. The guesthouse would never make a fortune, any more than the little businesses in the harbour. But it would be enough to keep them all going and prevent Mrs Bellamy from being forced to sell. It made no sense for the businesses to be ripped out and Enys Hall left to go to rack and ruin just so the Howellses, who were rich beyond anyone's wildest imagining, could have the convenience of a private harbour and fill the place with warehouses.

If only they could be certain that things would stay the same, that Tobias was too preoccupied in New York to return, and that the Howellses had lost interest in the harbour.

On a rare free afternoon, Jess walked over the cliffs to see Diana Catterell in St Ives.

'Your friend from London has written to ask to see some of my work for her new store,' said Diana, as they settled down for a cup of tea among the silverwork. 'I suspect I've you to thank for recommending me to Miss Fairbairn. She seemed to know all about me.'

'I told you she would be interested.'

'We'll see. Not only that, Mama has finally agreed to see me, although Papa still views me as a disgrace. I'm afraid he is convinced a woman can't possibly make a living on her own and I must be being supported by a rich lover.' She gave a wry smile. 'To him, financial independence in a woman is much the same thing as selling your body to the highest bidder. He sees the world as it was in the old queen's time. I'm going to have to accept he'll never change.'

'But at least your mother wants to meet you.'

'It's a relief, I have to confess. I hated being entirely cut off from all my family. Mama has finally admitted there are so few men left she's going to have to become reconciled to the fact that I am unlikely to marry. At least she promised to join me for afternoon tea when I next go to London.'

'I'm glad.'

'So am I. I love it here, but it can feel very lonely without a family nearby. The offer's still open, you know, Jess. If you find you can't use the workshop in the harbour for any reason. We always worked well together. I'm not sure I could teach you anything more, but I'd be more than happy for us to set up a workshop together.'

'If my designs sell.'

'Annette Fairbairn's emporium has only been open for a few weeks. You said she loved the silver clasps you sent her. I'm sure they will sell. You may even find in time you have to expand. I've been hearing good things about your father's harbour, that there are some beautiful old fishing lofts, much bigger and lighter than this cramped little space. We could always set up there if you didn't want to set up entirely on your own.'

'I love the idea,' said Jess, wistfully. But she couldn't think that far ahead. She'd had no word from Annette that there had been any interest in any of the hair clasps and pendants. In the silence, self-doubt had begun to creep in. Maybe they had been the wrong thing to start with. Maybe Giselle had simply been being kind. Why hadn't she seen they were hopelessly amateurish, without skill or merit? The kind of thing that would be passed over among the work of real craftsmen and women, the ones who had studied their craft for years at places like the Birmingham School of Jewellery.

She was so close to touching her dream! But at the same time, with no means of earning money from her work to replace the materials she had already used, let alone be able to support herself and be confident of supporting Dad in the future, it was still frustratingly out of reach. There were times when she feared that all her bravado had done was to condemn her to being a maid for the Bellamys, or rich families in St Ives, until her back was bent and her joints too arthritic to give satisfaction and she was replaced by a younger woman.

She tried to put such thoughts behind her as she left Dïana's workshop to accompany Frank and Charlotte to Charlotte's drawing class.

'I'll be your model again, if you like,' she said to a questioning tug of the hand from Charlotte, who smiled and nodded. As they reached the studio, Charlotte ran ahead to catch up with a girl about her own age, also making her way there with a satchel of painting materials over one shoulder.

'She's growing up,' said Frank.

'She's a long way to go yet. She'll be a schoolgirl for a while longer.'

'Yes, you are right. It's just that sometimes I catch myself thinking of her as a little girl and then I realise she is a baby no longer. She's growing tall, like our mother. And just as skilled. If our village had not been destroyed, she would have joined our mother painting miniatures, and I would have made frames and cabinets with Papa. Now we are so far away. At least I can earn a living in St Ives, but I am not sure I can see a life for Charlotte here.' He turned his head away from her. 'Maybe it is time we tried to go back to our village, to see what is there. It is still our home.'

A jolt went through her. 'To France?'

She could not see his expression. 'I have practical skills. I could work anywhere. It has been on my mind for a while. I wrote to the village priest. I was not certain if I would get a reply, but he is still there. He remembers us. The village has been rebuilt, some of the families have returned and they are eager for others to join them, to make the community again. I'm wondering if we return to France and Charlotte is surrounded by our own language again, that maybe she will speak. Our mother was well known as a miniaturist; it may be that Charlotte can be apprenticed to someone who knew her. That might find her a way of making a living, and finding peace of mind.'

Jess squashed the tightening in her heart. 'I think if Charlotte was my sister, I would do the same,' she admitted.

'I have to try, Jess. I don't know how else I can make sure she is independent. People can be cruel to those who are different, and even when she is safe she still has nightmares and days she cannot leave our rooms at all. I worry about her, if anything should happen to me.'

'But it won't.'

'I know. I hope. But I can't forget that life can be so uncertain.' He paused. 'There are things here that I will miss with all my heart, that I would never wish to leave. But sometimes it is better this way.'

'I understand, I was there when you arrived that night, remember? I know you have to do the best for Charlotte so that she can live her life, despite the terrible things happened to you both, things I can't even imagine. I want the best for her too.' She swallowed. He was doing the best he could for his sister, and she had no right to try and stop him, for all she longed to keep him there. 'Remember I'll always be here.'

'I'll remember,' he replied. But despite the warmth of his smile, it seemed the most final of goodbyes. As they went to join Charlotte, Jess felt a certainty, deep in her heart, that she would never see him again.

*

When she returned to the harbour later that evening, Jess found Morwenna sitting outside the forge.

'Jess, I've been waiting for you, I've been just dying to tell you – I wanted you to be the first to know. Your aunt has secured me a huge order for my embroidery from Barringtons for several new fashion lines. It's at least six months' work. It's so big I'll be able to rent a workshop of my own, and train up some of the girls who have an aptitude for embroidery.'

'That's wonderful, Morwenna!'

'If this continues, I should be able to expand. Mum's getting too old to work at the forge, and there is so little work these days anyway. I was so worried I was going to have to move away. I'm going to learn to drive a motorised van, so I can take the work to and from the train station. Isn't that just perfect?'

'It is,' said Jess, kissing her.

'And now all you need to do is to sell lots of your enamel work, and the harbour will be busy again, even busier than it was before. There's someone interested in taking over the bakery and Cook's niece is talking about setting up a tearoom in the harbour on her own. Not as fine as in Enys Hall, of course. But it will be perfect for people who don't want to go anywhere that grand.'

'Dad will be happy,' said Jess. 'He always said there needed to be more places than the Mermaid. And I won't say no to him being able to get his dinner there, if I'm busy,' she added, feeling slightly guilty.

'That's what she says. It'll be worth opening now there should be trade all year round. Sara says that's what they have in London: good restaurants where girls who work can get a meal cheaper than they can cook it.'

'Especially those who hardly have any space to cook at

all,' said Jess, remembering the little cooker perched on the landing in Annette's apartment.

'Although there's one person who won't be attending,' said Morwenna, turning her eyes to the road above them, where a dark-coloured Bentley had pulled to a stop in the lay-by overlooking the harbour.

Jess felt the breath leave her body as a figure stepped out from the driver's side and stood for a few minutes looking down. The slam of the door as he returned inside echoed round the little cove, followed by the roar of an engine racing towards Enys Hall.

'Looks like Tobias is back,' said Ben, joining them.

'And he doesn't seem best pleased with what has happened in his absence,' said Jess.

'I wouldn't like to be in Enys Hall tonight, when he sees what has being going on there, either,' said Morwenna.

'Or tomorrow, when I'll be cleaning there all day,' added Jess, gloomily.

Chapter Twenty-Five

'They'll be back,' said Diana a few weeks later, as she accompanied Jess to see Frank and Charlotte off at St Ives Station.

'I'm not sure,' said Jess. She had done her best to be cheerful, for Charlotte's sake, as if they really were only going to be away for a short time, but her heart felt hollow. 'They may find some of their family have survived and they wish to stay, especially if Charlotte finds more peace of mind there.'

'That may be. But even then, both of their lives are so much here. I can't imagine them anywhere else.'

'I'd be tempted to go with them,' growled an exasperated Rachel, when Jess returned to Enys Hall that afternoon.

'I thought you were enjoying this?'

'I am. Especially now we've had enquiries for next year from people as far away as France and Italy, and even a few Americans, too. It feels as if this could become a success. And it's good to see the harbour thriving again, like it used to be before the war.'

'It's Miss Louisa,' explained Cook, deep in the preparation of the evening meal.

Jess's heart sank. 'I thought she seemed to have accepted it all when she came back from London.'

'That was when she was certain Mr Tobias was about to come running and throw himself at her feet and she wouldn't have to be sullied by the grubbiness of commerce for long. That's the only reason she came home, if you ask me.'

'Oh,' said Jess. In the few days she had been back at Enys Hall, Louisa had made her presence felt, mainly in the form of additional work. Mrs Bellamy and Rachel kept their own rooms as clean and tidy as they could, even mending their own fires when needed, leaving as much time as possible for Jess to concentrate on cleaning the guest rooms between mending and reupholstering, while they gradually invested as much of their earnings as they dared in expanding the guest rooms. She always tried to shoot past Louisa's room, with clothes strewn carelessly over chairs and the bed and the demand for stockings to be mended and a bodice altered. At least Louisa had given up any idea that Jess should do her hair, demanding her mother should put it up to perfection instead.

'I hate living in a hotel,' complained Louisa, later that day.

'Then don't treat it like one,' retorted Rachel. 'Mama and I work hard to make this guesthouse a success and keep a roof over our heads. Maybe instead of fussing about your appearance, you could lift a finger to help us. Or at least entertain the guests. Talking to them at dinner time, rather than demanding you are served in your room, would be a start.'

'What am I supposed to talk to them about?'

'The harbour. St Ives. Cornwall. Answer their questions about the history of the area. Suggest places for them to visit. Listen to them talk about their day. It's not difficult.'

'Why would I want to do that? I'm not interested in middle-aged women taking walking tours, with their boots all caked in mud, who are never going to be married.'

'Since some of them have made themselves rich business-women or career women instead, you might learn something to your advantage. You listen long enough and quietly enough to Tobias when he's here.'

'But he knows about so many things, and he's really successful.'

'Oh, for heaven's sake,' said Rachel in exasperation, heading off to grab a broom.

Louisa, to everyone's surprise, did at least make an effort that evening, joining Miss Smithson and Miss Helsom, who were gleefully escaping Twickenham to ride their safety bicycles around the coast in the glorious autumn weather, returning browned and exhilarated and as often as not falling asleep over their syllabub or rice pudding.

'I heard you laughing,' said Rachel as she tidied away, before preparing the table for breakfast.

'They were interesting,' admitted Louisa, the customary sullen look on her face transformed into something more thoughtful. 'They both earn their own money.'

'And neither of them is poor.'

'They're not rich.'

'Aren't they?'

'You can tell from their coats.'

'I didn't mean that. Neither of them comes from money, and they earn very little as teachers; they both have to save hard to do the things they like. But at least they are free to do as they wish. I wouldn't say either of them was unhappy.'

'No.' Louisa considered this for a few minutes. 'But they don't have families of their own.'

'They have friendships,' said Rachel. 'I didn't really think about it until we had guests, but I seem to remember Mama relying on her female friends even more than Papa at times. There are many different ways of being happy.'

'That's because you've never known love,' retorted Louisa, sweeping out and up the stairs, back to her own room.

'I thought she was coming round to the idea that her engagement might be a long one, even after Tobias came back from America,' said Rachel, as her mother joined her to lay the table. 'I was hoping it might give her time to have second thoughts.'

'To be honest, my dear, I think she is just as determined to marry Tobias as ever. You were both stubborn children, far more so than the boys.' She sighed. 'A pity. Not that I want her to remain a widow, you understand. It would never suit her, not like some of our widowed guests, many of whom seem to have acquired a new lease of life, despite their grief. I'm afraid that, once they are married, Tobias will see it as an excuse to interfere on Louisa's behalf.'

'I'm quite sure he will. And I'm quite sure he won't approve of his wife's family running anything so lowly as a guesthouse.'

'Just as we seemed to be turning a corner, too. With the new rooms almost ready and the harbour attracting so many more visitors, we can finally support ourselves. In fact, I was thinking ...' Mrs Bellamy straightened the tablecloth and adjusted the salt cellar before placing a fresh vase of flowers, ready for the morning. 'I have a little money set aside. I was keeping it in case Aunt Julia refused to take us in, after all. I would never have risked it before, but if I sell my diamond necklace, which I never wear, there would be almost enough to pay back the investment from the Howellses. Thank goodness they didn't invest nearly as much as they promised, or it would have been quite impossible. As it is, we could well be able to pay back the rest next year, and finally be free of them.'

'Do you think that will stop Tobias doing his best to interfere? Despite everything, and all Papa's care, I'm sure he'll still think he has a right over the house and the harbour as Louisa's husband. And he'll enjoy throwing his weight around, especially as I'm quite sure Mr Howells doesn't allow him any say at home.'

'You don't know that, my dear.'

'From what Peter said—' She met her mother's frown. 'Oh, for heaven's sake, Mama, I never had any thought of stealing Peter away from Louisa. I wouldn't do that to a sister.'

'But you made sure he could confide in you. You spent nearly an hour with him the last night he was here, time he could have spent with Louisa.'

'The poor man was facing his own death, Mama. It didn't matter who I was. Helping those wretched people from the shipwreck that night opened a door, that's all. If he'd survived, I expect he'd have been horribly embarrassed at having let his guard slip. And besides, I think we all know his heart always lay elsewhere.'

'I don't want to hear you talking about that woman. Your sister has had enough to put up with in her life without having to be faced with her existence every day in every magazine and newspaper you open.'

'No, Mama,' said Rachel quietly, straightening a chair and taking the final tray down to the kitchens to help Jess with the washing up.

With the work done for the day, and Jess on her way home, Rachel went out into the garden.

She sighed. How could she explain to Mama that every day since she had returned from France, she had felt so guilty at being alive she hadn't been able to live. She looked down at the harbour. The distant waves became the rumble of thunder, the call of gulls the cries of desperately wounded men. The familiar horror crept back around her, winding itself, holding her tight, bringing with it the stench of rotting mud, putrefying flesh, and stifling filth.

With an effort, she breathed in deep, feeling the salt of the sea in her lungs. She forced her eyes open. There was just the quiet rush of the sea, the crash of waves against the harbour wall. She could feel life flooding through her veins.

Ben might no longer love her, but she had found a kind of peace. It might take working all hours of the day, with only snatched sleep, but she had found a way. These past weeks, as the work preparing the rooms had eased, and they had grown accustomed to the routine, she had found herself with more energy again, her mind working on plans for the future. She needed a greater sense of purpose to her life, more than running a guesthouse. The trouble was, if Tobias were still to walk in as Louisa's husband, that peace would be gone. Even if Mama managed to pay off the Howellses' investment, they still owned the land at the side to build their warehouses. The land Peter had left to Giselle. Tobias was bound to be keeping hold of it for something.

She couldn't blame Giselle for walking away from such a fight, even now she had the means. She was right: the only way to stay safe from Tobias's malice was to remain out of his notice. Easily pushed aside. The trouble was, if he was in the house, taking charge on the pretext that he was simply looking after his wife's interests, she knew she couldn't stay quiet for long. Tobias was the kind of man who would take delight in dismantling her, bit by bit, until she was trapped, too worn out with his bullying and manoeuvring to fight back.

The women who had stayed as guests had confirmed to her that she could make a living and that she had acquired so many skills that she could use. One or two were business-women, who might well point her in the direction of employment. Or she could even ask whether there was some kind of opening at Barringtons.

That would mean abandoning the harbour. Doing exactly

what Tobias had wanted all along. Louisa wouldn't question him, and Mama would simply do as she had always done, and keep the peace, even if she disagreed with what he was doing. Despite all her father's care to keep them legally safe, without someone there to fight running battles with Tobias the harbour would quickly lose its fledgling prosperity again.

Down below, Jess had stopped to talk to Mrs Wilkes. As she watched, Ben came out to join them. In the still evening air, their laughter drifted up towards her, tantalisingly out of reach.

However hard she tried, she couldn't help the feeling of inevitability about the three, already drawn together by so much. Survival, she remembered all too well, could overcome any barriers, and love, even if it was not there at the start, would always follow.

Ben had made it clear that his passion for her was over, that all they had shared in those days when life might have ended at any moment no longer had any meaning for him. How could she blame him, when she was the one who had destroyed his ability to follow his ambitions and the work he loved? No wonder he never wanted to see her again. She wished with every last fibre of her being that he might find happiness. But she couldn't bear to stay and watch it. She would fight Tobias with the last breath in her body to keep all those she loved safe, but even if she won she could not stay here. She could not condemn herself to inwardly dying, piece by piece.

Slowly, Rachel turned and made her way inside.

Chapter Twenty-Six

'I can't possibly complete that many!' Jess stared in alarm at Annette's letter. 'Especially in so short a time.'

'Of course you can,' said Ben. 'It's the kind of opportunity that might never come again.'

'But Enys Hall…'

'Rachel will understand. They'll manage. Jess, this could earn you enough to set up your own business or join in partnership with Diana. This could be a proper start for you. You've got to take the chance.'

'Yes, you're right.' She took a deep breath, steadying herself. Beneath the terror of failure, excitement had begun to stir. 'Thank you.'

'I haven't done anything.'

'You have faith in me.' Her determination was back again. This was the chance she'd worked towards, the reason she had stubbornly refused to take the security of the job offered at Barringtons. She wasn't about to fail now. 'It just caught me by surprise, that's all. I thought that was it when I didn't hear from Annette. I was so sure she was too embarrassed to tell me no one was interested in buying my work. I was quite resigned to never having any orders again.'

'Didn't you say Miss Fairbairn was busy getting her shop ready?' He nodded at the pages of a ladies' magazine Annette had enclosed with her letter. 'And there are these.'

Jess stared down at them. In her shock at suddenly finding

herself overwhelmed with orders, she had barely glanced at them. There were two magazines and a newspaper, all dated within the past week. One showed Giselle Harding wearing the central part of the silver clasp in the form of a headband, the others featuring her delicate profile, the clasp her only adornment, holding her hair in place.

'So she really meant it when she said she loved it.'

'Of course she did, you fool. And she must know that this is the best way of helping you. This is your chance, Jess. You've got to take it.'

Jess nodded, mind working fast. 'If I'm going to complete them all in time, I'm going to need help to form the shapes so I can concentrate on the enamelling.'

'I can do some, but I'll be too slow.'

'But that will help me, Ben.'

'Very well. But I think you should also ask Diana.'

'I can't take her from her own work!'

'Didn't you say she had already completed the earrings ordered by Miss Fairbairn? Whenever I've spoken to her, it seems she's holding her own but not overwhelmed with other orders for her silverwork. If you are thinking you might set up in business together, this might be a good test.'

'Test?'

'Until now, you have always been the assistant. This might be a good test of seeing how it works the other way round.'

'I don't want Diana to be my assistant. I wouldn't insult her.'

'It's still a good test of whether you can work together. And you do need help.'

'But I need to get going straight away.'

'Don't worry, you can send me to speak to her on your behalf, and source the materials you need, so you can concentrate on getting these done.' His smile was a little sad. 'I can be your assistant for this, too.'

Diana returned later that day with Ben, more than happy to help. For the next week, she stayed in Aunt Sara's old room, helping Ben with the cutting and shaping of the silver base, ready for Jess to work on the finer details and the enamelling.

'I don't ever want to do anything that fast again,' said Jess, just after dawn one morning, as the orders were finally finished and packed up securely for Diana to take to London on the morning train.

'But you wouldn't refuse.'

'Certainly not,' said Jess. They had worked through most of the night to get the pieces finished on time. She ached all over, her eyes itched, and all she wanted was to sleep, rather than to drag herself off to Enys Hall for a day of cleaning bedrooms and chopping vegetables. But, at least for now, she had to be practical.

'All ready,' said Diana, placing the parcel deep in her bag. 'Mama said in her letter that she would be pleased to see me. I'll be back in a few days, hopefully with more orders for both of us.'

'Let's hope so,' said Jess.

'Done him the world of good,' remarked Mrs Wilkes, as Jess removed her apron and hastily tidied her hair before making her way to Enys Hall. 'More like his old self.'

'I'm glad.'

'Although I'm selfish enough to wish he'd be staying.'

'Staying?'

'Didn't he tell you? Mind you, I suppose this ain't the time, you being rushed off your feet. He's been offered his old post, teaching at the Birmingham School of Jewellery. I didn't think he'd write to them, but something must have persuaded him to swallow his pride. They want him to start next month.'

'Oh,' said Jess. Emptiness opened up inside. She couldn't imagine working without Ben's reassuring presence in the workshop. But that was being selfish; and for all he had tried to hide it, she had felt his sadness too. 'I'm glad for him. He is a wonderful teacher.'

'Aye, that he is,' said Mrs Wilkes. 'With him able to earn a living and Morwenna doing so well with her embroidery, I'll see them both settled. I'll miss my Ben, though.'

'You could always go with him.'

Mrs Wilkes shook her head. 'It's not home, no more. My life is here. I've friends here, and Morwenna. I've still work I can do. I don't know how I'd live if I couldn't look out over the sea every day and breathe in that good air. I'd even miss the storms; they make me feel alive. Besides, a young man don't need his mother at home to watch his every move, even if she tries not to. I hoped once he'd be back to help his dad and then take over the business. But from the first time he came back, I knew he would never be here to stay. And especially now. His life has been changed from everything he thought it might be. I think, mebbe in the city, he's more of a chance of finding a new way.'

'I'm sure you are right,' said Jess, sadly.

Mrs Wilkes grunted. 'There aren't many, these days, who're born here and die here. Change is never easy. Can make you feel you are being left behind. I can't bear the thought of him leaving, but I know it's what's right fer Ben and I can't stand in his way. But I shall miss him.'

As Jess made her way up to Enys Hall, the October mist lying low on the fields was clearing into a brilliant sunny day. The chill in the air slowly eased with the rising sun. She breathed in deep, feeling the warmth on her face. Despite her hasty wash in the pump outside the smithy, she felt sweaty and grubby. The sea had never looked so inviting.

She could feel how much things were changing all around her. Aunt Sara was building a successful life for herself in London. Frank was gone, and now Ben, too. After the rush of working with Ben and Diana to complete the clasps on time, she felt empty, as if she was being left behind, still stubbornly following a dream that might leave her struggling to make an uncertain living for the rest of her days, while life passed her by, without any hope of love or a family of her own. Deep loneliness settled inside her.

'Don't be an idiot,' she scolded herself. 'You're just tired, that's all.'

As she reached the top of the path, she stopped to catch her breath. Around her the patchwork of fields gleamed between the hedgerows. A pleasure boat was setting off across the bay, while below her, the shops around the harbour were beginning to get ready for the day. Dad was already heading towards the harbourmaster's office, stopping to greet the fishermen on the quay. The echo of their customary banter on the size of the fish and the weather drifted up towards her, followed by a burst of male laughter. Cook's niece was wiping down the tables set outside the tea rooms, accompanied by the delicious aroma of baking bread and the fruitiness of tea loaf.

Morwenna, who had left the forge before dawn to finish the intricate embroidery for a wedding dress, emerged from her workshop, hands in the small of her back, stretching herself out. Jess smiled as the young man who had recently set up in leatherworking in the next workshop appeared, as he often did on fine days, to join her. It was still too early for the day's visitors to have stirred. As the little boat set out towards

St Ives in search of passengers, the two settled down at one of the newly wiped tables, deep in conversation, to the almost instant appearance of teapot and cups, accompanied by plates and a butter dish. The smell of toast mingled with the rest of the morning's smells. Her stomach had been in too much of a knot to grab more than a half-drunk cup of tea in the rush to make sure the clasps were polished to perfection.

Mrs Wilkes was right. Among the old and the few of the young, like Morwenna, who had decided to stay, there was at last new blood in the harbour. Young energy, some from St Ives and Penzance, others from further away. All of them had known grief and loss, and many, like the painter with the damaged hand who was setting up in his customary place on the quay, had seen things on battlefields far away that had changed their futures and would haunt their dreams for ever.

Jess sighed. She should be triumphant, full of gleeful energy, after her worst doubts had been banished and she had gained so many orders, and, with the help of Ben and Diana, been able to fill them in time. But instead she felt only sadness.

'Pull yourself together, you fool,' she muttered aloud, as she resumed her journey. She had notebooks of sketches, plenty of ideas to work on. Today, she was just drained from the rush of getting the hair clasps finished on time, and dreading a day of mindless drudgery. She hadn't worked so hard to get this opportunity to give up now. She pushed away any doubts that she had not completed the clasps to a high enough standard, so that the women who had made orders on the strength of Giselle's recommendation would be disappointed, leaving Annette out of pocket and no further orders to come her way.

She had put her heart and soul into producing her best work, she reminded herself. If Annette's clients loved them, she would earn enough from the clasps to be able to invest in more materials and better equipment, as well as supporting herself, and Dad if need be, for the next few months at least. Besides, if her venture didn't succeed, she had the option of finding work as a cleaner in St Ives, or swallowing her pride and asking Aunt Sara to employ her in London.

She still had choices. There were plenty of women far worse off than she would ever be, grieving the loss of a lover or husband, facing a life of struggle to make ends meet, without any hope of escape from their loneliness. At least in the harbour she was surrounded by those who had known her all her life, cared for her and would always keep her safe. And as for love …

She was so deep in thought, she barely heard the motor car racing up the driveway behind her. A horn was sounded, sending her stumbling on the gravel.

'Daydreaming will get you killed one day, you know.' The vehicle slowed to a halt next to her. 'And I'd be the one held responsible.'

'Good morning, Mr Howells,' she said tersely, ignoring Tobias's mocking grin.

'Late again for Cook, I see. Perhaps I should go and speak to her, explain that I was the one who detained you. I wouldn't like you to lose your post.'

'That's very kind of you, sir,' she replied evenly, teeth gritted. 'But not in the least necessary. Cook is aware that I was to be detained in the harbour this morning and so will be starting later than usual today. It's all quite in order. So, if you'll excuse me …' She set off again, aware of the Bentley keeping pace with her every step.

'I bet they don't know you've been meeting Giselle Harding,' he remarked, voice hardening. 'Or making some kind of costume jewellery for her to adorn herself.'

Don't rise to the bait. Don't rise to the bait. She bit the inside of her lip. 'I think you must be mistaken, Mr Howells.'

'I'm taking Miss Louisa out for the day. I'm sure she would like to hear what our local female blacksmith has been up to.' He picked up an open magazine on the passenger seat and waved it at her. 'I'm sure she'd like to see this, and your name there as the maker, bold as brass. I can hardly expect my fiancée to stay in a household that thinks it's acceptable to employ someone who is making trinkets for her late husband's mistress. I should have known. Giselle always was cheap.'

'If you'll excuse me ...'

'Immorality sticks, you know. Taints everything it touches.'

'Unless it's a man,' she retorted before she could stop herself. 'Then it's a natural need and he is not tainted at all.'

His eyes narrowed. 'As I said, immorality taints everything it touches. I'm not sure, once we are married, I can bear to allow my wife, or her poor widowed mother and spinster sister, to continue to be taken in by a girl prepared to sell to such a woman the fruits of her trade. A woman who once seduced my brother away from his family with her charms. I'm not sure I'd want my wife to be so sullied.'

His voice was bitter, the smooth veneer of superiority cracking a little. It sounded to her as if things had gone no better in America than they had in the factory near London, and his father was not best pleased. Jess bit the words back before they could escape her.

If he chose to blame others, rather than face himself, he would always need to find someone in no position to fight back. He knew, as well as she did, that she could not afford to defend herself. She still had rent to pay, Dad needed to keep his job. Until she knew for certain the clasps had been actually bought by the women who had ordered them, and her work was good enough to risk building up her own business, she had no choice. She could see in his face his enjoyment of his power over her, a soothing balm to any humiliation he might be experiencing since his return to live under his father's roof.

They had reached the front of the house. 'Good day, Mr Howells,' she said, as calmly as she could manage, turning away from the driveway, over the grass towards the kitchens.

As she reached the door, she heard Tobias draw up in front of the main door, throwing orders at Alice, who had only recently been hired by Mrs Bellamy, and whose hunched-up shoulders already had the look of a longing to flee into the nearest woods, never to be seen again.

The harbour's glimpse of peace was over.

Chapter Twenty-Seven

Jess managed to stay out of Tobias's way as he waited for Louisa while making stilted conversation with Rachel and Mrs Bellamy, who were surely itching to get rid of him so they could begin the day's work in earnest.

At least the party of women painters had set out early, straight after breakfast, to find a good vantage point on the cliffs, and so were in no danger of meeting him.

She could feel the relaxation in the air as the motor car finally disappeared into the distance.

'He was talking about setting a wedding date,' said Rachel gloomily, as she joined Jess in preparing the rooms for their next set of guests, due to arrive that evening. 'Now all we're going to hear from Louisa for the next month is wedding clothes.'

'At least there are plenty of guests for Enys Hall,' said Jess.

'Yes, that's true. And their numbers are increasing, even for the winter months, when I thought we might have none at all. I'd begun to think we could make a go of this, but you could see on Tobias's face he'll do everything he can to prevent us from continuing.'

'But there's nothing he can do to stop you.'

'No,' said Rachel. 'But I bet he'll still try.'

*

It was as she was making her way to Enys Hall a few mornings later that Jess could smell bonfires filling the air. Thick smoke drifted across the harbour, sending the men indulging in an early breakfast at the tea rooms scurrying inside.

As she reached the grounds, she found Rachel standing in the garden watching proceedings. 'He's clearing the land Peter left to Giselle, as if he owns it.'

'I thought that's what it must be.'

'The smoke's bad enough up here, heaven knows what it must be like for the businesses in the harbour.'

'There's been talk…' Jess hesitated. 'I hoped he was wrong, but Dad says there's been talk in the Mermaid that Tobias is wanting to build some kind of manufacturing business there.'

'Manufacturing? What kind of manufacturing?'

'I'm not sure. Dad usually tries not to ask questions so they don't know how closely he's listening, if you see what I mean. But that was the talk.'

'In any case, it doesn't really matter, does it,' said Rachel, turning back as the next roll of smoke headed towards the little businesses. 'I'm sure Tobias doesn't care whether it makes money – despite what his father might think – so long as it's the noisiest and most foul-smelling he can find, I would think. The kind to make visitors avoid the place and working there unpleasant. And he knows there's nothing we can do about it.'

'Or thinks there isn't,' said Jess. She met Rachel's eyes.

'I don't want to drag Giselle into this.'

'But I think she'd want to know.'

'You are right, of course.' Rachel resumed snipping a bunch of late-blooming roses with her secateurs as Louisa stepped out into the garden. She lowered her voice. 'It'll take too long to send a letter to America. I'll make an excuse to go into St Ives and send a telegram as soon as breakfast is over. It's a beautiful morning, isn't it?' she called cheerfully to Louisa, who was wrinkling her nose as the smell of burning began to pervade the garden.

The clearing of the brambles and saplings that had overgrown the old meadows went on for the rest of the week. The group of painters were not best pleased at having to change their vantage point to avoid the effects of the smoke, while the two friends on a walking holiday expressed their disappointment at not being able to linger in the grounds of an evening, after they had come so far for the benefits of peace and fresh air.

Rachel apologised profusely, but there was no point in trying to reason with Tobias. Knowing he was irritating their guests would only encourage him to build bigger bonfires. At least they no longer had to endure his presence every morning and evening. After his first flurry of attentions, he abandoned Louisa for several weeks, leaving her tearful and irritable with fear that he had changed his mind after all.

Once their guests had gone out for the day, you could cut the tension in the air with a knife.

In the harbour, too, the unease was catching. With much of the scrubland removed, the sound of spades and pickaxes filled the air from dawn to dusk as Tobias' smen began to clear the ground in earnest.

'The talk in the Mermaid is that it's to be a munitions factory,' said Dad one evening, as Jess returned wearily from Enys Hall.

'But the war's over!'

'There's still plenty of trade for munitions,' he replied gloomily. 'The Howellses still have their factory near London; the talk is that they wish to expand. It could be just a rumour, of course. But personally, I can't see a better way of clearing the harbour than having explosives so close; and who'd wish to stay at Enys Hall, when they might be blown to smithereens? People have had enough of that. All we want is peace and quiet.'

'Do you really think he'd build a munitions factory?' said Ben, joining them on the harbour wall.

'It'll turn a profit and provide work,' said Dad. 'Not that anyone from the harbour will see any of it, mark my words. And he's enough money to throw at any scheme he wishes. I don't expect he's particularly concerned whether it's a success or not. We've defied him, so we must be punished.' He indicated Enys Hall, where Rachel was standing in the garden looking down on proceedings. 'Them, and all. If you ask me, he'll see it as a small price to pay to get control of the harbour. That's the point, after all.'

'You must be glad you're leaving,' said Jess to Ben, as Dad returned inside the harbourmaster's office.

'I'm glad to be getting a wage again.' Ben was still frowning at the men working away on the other side of the harbour. 'I don't like the thought of abandoning you all.'

'But there's nothing you can do, or anyone can do.'

'Maybe.' He glanced up at Rachel, who was still standing in the gardens of Enys Hall. 'I still don't like the thought of what might happen here.'

Jess followed his gaze. 'There might still be a way of stopping him.'

'I can't see how. He has the land and the money. He's already making life uncomfortable for everyone around. He holds all the cards.'

Jess bit her lip. 'I suppose so.' She longed to tell him about Giselle, that there might yet be someone with money and influence on their side. But that was to break a confidence, and besides, Rachel had not yet heard back from Giselle.

Perhaps she was prepared to simply let the land go and let Tobias have his way.

She found Ben scrutinising her. 'What will you do, Jess?'

'I'm not sure. I'll stay here as long as I can. I don't want to leave them at Enys Hall, but Tobias has made it quite clear he wants to get rid of me. It looks like I'm going to have to move away again to find a workshop.'

He cleared his throat. 'You could always find a post with me, in Birmingham. The school would love your designs. I'm sure you could find a post teaching. That might be a better way of supporting yourself while you set up your own business, rather than working as a maid. I can see how exhausted you are at the end of each day. I'll give you a recommendation with pleasure.'

'Thank you.' A question crackled in the air. She took a quick glance at his face. His expression was unreadable. If this was an offer of love, it was a strange one. Confusion surged up inside. They worked well together, with the ease of good companions who had known each other all their lives. She was well aware that in the eyes of the harbour they were a perfect couple, despite Ben's disability. Dad clearly assumed that the banns would be read out before many weeks were out.

She thought of Ben leaving, of being here without him. The sense of loneliness was intense. Surely anything was better than that? There were plenty of companionable marriages in the harbour. Maybe she was a fool to dream of more. Yet she did. She couldn't settle for second best, for a life without passion, any more than she could live without her enamel work. She had loved Ben for as long as she could remember; she always would. But not as a lover. She was quite sure he had never viewed her in that way either.

And there was something else ... She turned her gaze up

to where Rachel was still watching them. The locket. The locket he had been gazing at so intently that day in the workshop. There had been something so familiar about it, it had niggled away at her mind ever since. She should have recognised the Russian *cloisonné* forget-me-nots of the locket she had watched Ben mend for Rachel before he went to help the wounded in France. Deep inside, something fell into place.

Behind them, Dad was closing up the office, ready to walk back with them.

'You'll consider it, then?' Ben was saying.

She nodded absently. 'I need to think things over.'

'Good.'

'Thank you for the offer.' Whatever she felt, whatever choices she had to make, she couldn't bear to be ungracious, especially now she understood how much his return to Birmingham was costing him. 'That was very thoughtful of you.'

'Aye, well,' he said, as if barely hearing her. His eyes were back on the gardens of Enys Hall. But Rachel had vanished.

A few days later, the morning dawned clear and cloudless.

'No building work, I see,' remarked Mrs Wilkes, who was sitting outside the forge with her early morning cup of tea as Jess made her way up to Enys Hall. 'Weren't none last night, neither. Funny that, when they've been working day and night.'

'It is odd,' agreed Jess, turning to look across the harbour. She was tired from a restless night of tossing and turning and her mind was fuzzy. She had stumbled out of the cottage in a daze, barely taking note of her surroundings.

'Blessed relief, if you ask me,' said Mrs Wilkes.

'Yes,' said Jess, all thought of tiredness gone. She couldn't believe Tobias would have stopped causing them inconvenience of his own volition. Either his father had stepped in, or ... She took a deep breath of clean sea air, untainted by dust or the drifting of smoke. Maybe, just maybe. She barely dared hope.

The guests at Enys Hall were delighted. As she took their breakfast to the dining room, Jess found the group of lady artists happily planning a day in the harbour, instead of traipsing along the cliffs to find a less polluted view.

'Let's hope it stays that way,' said Rachel, scrambling eggs under Cook's watchful eye. 'I wouldn't put it past Tobias to lull us into a false sense of security, let everyone relax and start up with his games again.'

Jess couldn't quite believe it either. Wherever she was in the house, she couldn't help but peer down into the harbour to check it hadn't been an illusion or just a brief break in proceedings.

But the peace and stillness remained all day. It was there for the rest of the week, much to the delight of the artists, who soon forgot the inconvenience of the earlier part of their stay, enthusing each evening at the play of light on water and the charming reflections of the fishing boats in the harbour, with the occasional majestic schooner that seemed to have taken on the form of an adventurer, or even a pirate, to add romance to their paintings.

Only Louisa avoided the general sense of relief, once again keeping to her room for much of the time and barely exchanging a word with anyone on the brief occasions she emerged.

'Tobias hasn't been to see her since the work on the land stopped,' said Rachel. 'I was so hoping Giselle might choose to intervene if she knew what was going on, but now I'm afraid he's making Louisa pay.'

'Maybe that's a good thing?' said Jess. 'I mean, that it might show her what he's really like.'

'I do hope so. I wish it would give her pause for thought and make her see sense, but all she keeps saying is that he will marry her and take her away from all this. The trouble is, I don't think she'll ever become reconciled to Enys Hall being a guesthouse. I thought she'd enjoyed talking to some of the guests, but I'm afraid that all changed when Tobias came back. It's as if he has some hold over her. He seems to have found the perfect way to harness her emotions and use them for his own ends. The longer he stays away, the better.'

There was no sign of Tobias, either at Enys Hall or the harbour, as one week stretched into two. The next time she went to visit Diana in St Ives, Jess found there was no sign of any of the Howellses at their summer home.

'They left last week,' said Diana. 'That's what one of the housekeepers from a neighbouring villa told one of my pupils. The whole family packed up and went to London, when they usually stay until just before Christmas. And all the staff have been dismissed, even the housekeeper who keeps the place aired during the winter months. Maybe Cornwall has lost interest for them and they've found somewhere they consider more fashionable, like Italy, or the South of France.'

'Let's hope so,' said Jess.

'Have you had any news from Frank? It still feels strange not seeing them in St Ives.'

Jess shook her head. 'No one seems to have heard anything from him. I hoped Frank might have written to let us know if they had found their village. Their landlady seemed certain they would have been back by now if they'd intended to return. Perhaps they have found their family, after all.'

'It may be for the best,' said Diana. 'Although I'll be sad not to see them again. Charlotte seemed so settled here. But something was preventing her from speaking, even after all this time. I feel certain her brother would do anything to give her a future.'

'I'm sure he would,' said Jess, steering the conversation back towards Diana's latest designs.

'Still no word from Annette?' asked Rachel a few days later, as she and Jess clipped the hedges threatening to obscure the view from the sunniest part of the garden while the guests were out for the day.

'Not a thing.'

'I've heard nothing from Giselle either. Maybe she wasn't the cause of the building work being stopped, after all. I can't help thinking I should never have tried to drag her into this.' She glanced up towards the house. 'There was an article in one of Louisa's magazines all about how Giselle is to be the star of a new moving picture. It's supposed to be the most expensive ever made. I'm afraid Giselle might well be too caught up in her own work to worry about a small piece of Cornish land. The article was saying it would make or break the stars and the studio.'

'But something has sent the Howellses back to London.'

'That's true, and without Louisa. They've never allowed her outside their influence when Tobias has been away. It almost feels as if she's no longer of any use to them.'

'That's horrible!'

'I'm afraid even my mother concedes that they are not very pleasant people,' replied Rachel gloomily. 'The more I think about it, the more I understand Peter was trying his best not to be like them. I don't like what he did to my sister, but Giselle was right. For all his faults, he was the best of the lot. At least he cared about Louisa, and tried to be fair to her as much as he could, and Giselle too, when he knew he might die. All Tobias and his father seem to be interested in is the bricks and mortar of the harbour and making more money than anyone could possible spend in a hundred lifetimes. Which I suppose is what Giselle is doing, too.'

'Only because she knows what it's like to have nothing.'

'But I can't help wondering, especially after reading those articles about the glamorous lifestyles of the richest movie stars, whether it might be impossible not to be caught up in it and forget anything else. Not that I would blame Giselle. She's risked everything to get where she is. And I can understand if all she wants to do is to forget the past.' She took the pruning saw to a particularly persistent branch of forsythia that had grown tall and straggly, threatening to have ideas above its station and take over one side of the garden altogether. 'It could just be that it would take too much investment, or they've found a more convenient place for their warehouses. There must be plenty of places more accessible from London than out here in St Ives.'

'Yes,' said Jess, collecting the clippings into a wheelbarrow to be deposited on the compost heap in a discreet corner of the grounds to avoid any possible offence to the sensitive noses of the lady artists.

She wished she could share Rachel's optimism. As she pushed the overflowing wheelbarrow towards the far side of the gardens, she couldn't dispel a niggling feeling that it couldn't be so simple. From up here, the harbour looked quiet and peaceful in the afternoon sun. The murmur of voices drifted up from the visitors sitting at the tables outside the tea rooms on the quay. The fishing boats were being prepared for the night's catch, with the mending of nets being closely observed by a painter on the quay. A group of walkers were disembarking from the boat ferrying visitors to and from St Ives, being pointed in the direction of the cliff walk to make their way back, while passengers were waiting to return to their hotels and guesthouses at the end of a day wandering the cliffs and, if rumours were true, swimming in the more secluded coves.

She emptied the wheelbarrow and made her way back to Rachel. The sun was beginning to lose its heat. They didn't have long before their guests would be back for afternoon tea in the garden and exchange stories of their day. A movement caught her eye. On the road to St Ives, a group of female cyclists was making its way towards Enys Hall.

'That looks like our guests,' said Rachel, hastily removing the last of the branches. 'We'll have to finish these tomorrow.'

'I'll let Cook know to start making the tea,' said Jess absently. The cyclists were passing the lay-by above the harbour, where a black Bentley was parked. It was the glint of low sun on glass that caught her attention. As the cyclists passed, the vehicle's door was slammed, sharp in the still evening air, before it set off slowly in the direction of St Ives.

Jess watched it go. Motor cars were less of a novelty these days, especially with the wealthy summer visitors revelling in the freedom of being able to go wherever they pleased. There had to be more than one Bentley on the roads of Cornwall these days. All the same, there was something slow and deliberate about the way it made its way along that sent a familiar unease creeping down her spine.

Chapter Twenty-Eight

'But you can't still want to marry him!' Rachel stared at Louisa in exasperation. 'After all he has done. Are you really so desperate to get away from us?'

'Of course I'm not.'

Rachel glanced at her sister's blotchy face, the mouth tight in a sullen line. A jolt went through her. She knew that look. She'd seen it before when they were children, when Simon dared them to follow him over the rocks above the far end of the cove, with just the sea beneath. Rachel had followed her elder brother without question, determined not to give into his scorn that girls couldn't do anything. It was the day she'd discovered the exhilaration of holding on for dear life, feet feeling for the next foothold, death beneath. She'd despised her little sister for being terrified of falling but too afraid of Simon to defy the recklessness of her brother.

Then, it had been Oliver who had reached Louisa, frozen at the point of no return. He had been the one with nothing to prove, who had understood that Louisa, in her fear, was bound to fall. It had been Oliver who had taken her back to safety. She remembered the white-hot anger on his face. Simon had sported a black eye for several weeks afterwards.

Things had gone back to normal for the rest of the summer, but the family had not returned to the way it had been before. The brothers had never quite been as close after that. It had been the beginning of Simon joining walking parties in the Lake District and climbing in Snowdonia, always pushing himself to reach higher and conquer the more perilous rock faces.

'Louisa,' she said gently. Louisa burst into tears. Rachel silently handed her a handkerchief and waited until the sobs died down.

Guilt shot through her. She had never had Oliver's patience with their sister. Perhaps because Louisa was just the kind of daughter any parent would desire. Rachel had been the troublesome one, the one who didn't fit the expected mould. The one who caused embarrassment to their father and mortification to their mother, as if her rebellion had been a reflection on them. Louisa had always been the favourite, the one eager to please. Longing to stay the favourite at any cost, because there seemed to be no other option, could lead a woman into very dangerous waters.

'It's not about winning or losing,' she said, as Louisa's weeping subsided into muffled hiccups. 'You know me. I'm an oddity. I always will be. I can't possibly win anything. No man is ever going to look at me twice if you are in the room.'

'But you can do things,' said Louisa between sniffles. 'You know what you want. You don't seem to need love at all.'

'Of course I need love. I'm like anyone else. I feel I'm dying inside when I think of what might have been, if things had been different. Why do you think I keep myself busy? Do you really think it's because I have no heart for anything else?'

'But …' Louisa came to a halt. 'You've never been engaged.'

'That doesn't mean I don't know about love.'

Louisa's eyes widened. 'You mean, you had a love affair? A real one?'

'As real as you can get.'

'But then you should have married him.'

'It was impossible.'

'Did you truly love him?' asked Louisa in a small voice.

At the look on her sister's face, Rachel's heart began to break. 'With all my heart and soul. I still do. I always will.'

'Did he die?'

Rachel shook her head. 'But it's utterly impossible. Don't ask me why.'

Slowly, Louisa leant against her. Rachel could feel the heat of her tear-stained face against her shoulder.

'They are horrible,' she said at last. 'The Howellses, I mean. They treat me as if I'm just a silly girl. Which I suppose I am.'

'No, you're not. You know you're not, Louisa. You're just trying to be the daughter our parents wanted, the wife Peter expected you to be, that's all. You don't have to be like that for the rest of your life. Why else do you think I'm cleaning like a demon and being shouted at by Cook when she gets in a temper? It's only so that you and me and Mama can all have choices. If we can earn our own income, none of us need depend on anyone else. We can be free. Maybe even be free to love who we choose.'

'He never loved me.' A deep sob shook Louisa, so utterly unlike her usual dramatics that Rachel went cold inside. 'Peter, I mean. I was just convenient. Peter would have left me in the end, even if I'd stayed married to him until the day I died. He only married me because he was afraid of his father. I can't blame him, I'm afraid of his father too. He's got a way of looking at you as if you are nothing. I hate it.'

'Then don't go back, Louisa. You don't have to. I know you don't enjoy having the guesthouse here, but it doesn't have to be for ever. We are starting to earn enough so the three of us could move into one of the empty houses on the other side of the harbour, and we could hire someone to

288

help Mama manage Enys Hall so you and I can do what we want. We don't have to decide what to do now. At least we'd know we had a roof over our heads. It might be smaller, but the gardens are pretty and we could chose one that is quite private. You need never see a guest again.'

'But then what would I do?'

'Anything you wish. Don't you see, that's a luxury most women don't have in this world? Jess and Alice need to work every hour of the day just to buy food and pay the rent. That's how most women live, some in desperate circumstances where they can barely survive. The guesthouse has given us the luxury of being able to choose what we do. You don't even have to do anything. You can sit and read all day, if you wish.'

'But I have to do something.'

'Then help Mama. I thought you enjoyed talking to our guests. You seemed to like that they were making their own living.'

'But I don't know what to do. I'm not good at anything. Not like you.'

'I wasn't born good at anything, Louisa. I'm always asking myself if I'm doing things wrong or if I'm just being an interfering old busybody. I haven't found what I want to do with my life either. But I'm determined to find a way of having a purpose to my life, just as I had out in France. There are hundreds of thousands of women who are widows, or have lost the love of their lives, or who will never have a chance to be married. We are all having to try to find a new way of living.'

'Yes,' said Louisa, slowly. Her face had softened into that of the child Rachel remembered. Maybe her suspicion had been ill-founded. She began to hope Tobias hadn't succeeded in bending Louisa completely to his will.

Then Louisa's face crumpled. 'But I can't. I have to marry him. I'll just have to go with him. And now Mr Howells is saying that if the harbour doesn't succeed, he'll blame Tobias. He keeps on saying he's useless and how Peter was worth ten of him and he's threatening to send him to some tiny place somewhere in South America where there's only jungle.'

'South America?' Rachel stared at her. 'Is that where you want to live?'

'Of course not. I tried to tell them that, but they don't listen and Tobias just got cross. He doesn't want to go there either; he wants to stay here, look after the harbour and build the new factory on Peter's land so we can all be rich again. He's got to succeed. Mr Howells said he's given him enough chances and he won't be made a fool of again, and if he fails at this, it's his cousin Robert who is going to be put in charge of everything when Mr Howells retires, not Tobias at all. Which is horrible.'

'Do you love him?'

There was a moment's silence.

'Yes. Yes, of course I do. Why else would I marry him?'

'That doesn't sound like passionate love to me.'

'What you mean is that you think he could only ever want to marry me so he could have some influence over the harbour. Just like Peter.'

'No! Of course I'm not saying that. And anyhow, who cares about the Howellses. They don't matter. Even if we still couldn't survive without their investment, I'd much rather go and live with Aunt Julia and find a way of supporting you and Mama by working than seeing you unhappy. They might be as rich as can be, but I can't see that they do anything with their wealth, not even to make themselves contented. All they seem to want to do is to gather more for its own sake, which is all a bit pointless if you ask me. I'm saying it's your choice. The Howellses don't matter. Forget everything else, just listen to your own heart.'

'But I have to marry him. I have to.' Louisa burst into tears again. 'He said it would be all right. That he'd look after me. He said I couldn't love him if I didn't want to sleep with him, and he'd soon find someone else. And it wasn't as if I hadn't done it before, and it would be all right, nothing would happen and, in any case, he'd always stand by me.'

The fear settled into cold, hard certainty. 'Louisa—'

'Don't look at me like that. Don't you dare judge me.'

'I'm not.'

'Or feel sorry for me. I can't bear it.'

'I'm not feeling sorry for you, Louisa, believe me. And I'm the last person to judge you. I only want to help. Are you quite sure you're with child?'

Louisa nodded miserably. 'I so wanted a baby when Peter was alive, so he would stay with me and forget that horrible woman. It didn't happen then, and I never thought it would happen so soon. Besides, we were going to be married, so it didn't matter. And I had to show I loved him. I didn't want him to prefer some little tart of an actress, just like Peter did.'

'Oh, Louisa.' Rachel hugged her tight. 'If Tobias truly loved you, he'd never have threatened you with that. Peter was in love with Giselle for years before he met you. Besides, there was a war, when so many hasty marriages took place. This was never going to be the same.'

'But Tobias has been telling me he's going to leave me. He says he won't have a wife associated with anything as low as a guesthouse. So if he doesn't marry me, it will be all your fault.'

'That's rich, coming from a glorified shopkeeper. That's what he is, Louisa, for all he might dress up those stores in London and New York as fancy emporiums. He's a shopkeeper whose family is in manufacturing. So he can't look down his nose at us, or anyone, however much money he has.' She looked at the misery on her sister's face. 'Does anyone else know you're pregnant?'

'No.'

'Not even Tobias?'

'I'll have to tell him soon.'

'Or you needn't tell him at all.'

'I couldn't!'

'I don't mean try to get rid of the baby, or send it away. Mama and I are earning enough to support you. We could always say you are away working with refugees, and you could come back when you are ready. We could find someone nearby to look after the child, so you could still see it. Or you could say you've adopted one in Peter's memory to give a refugee child a home.'

'There will be talk. Everyone will know.'

'But they can't prove it. Tell everyone it was because it was a passing resemblance to Peter that made you want to adopt the child in the first place. Even if anyone does suspect, it'll soon be forgotten. You'd be surprised at how many children are passed off as that of a grandmother or an aunt if you look closely.'

'But everyone'll talk. They'll know. They'll say I was stupid. Or immoral, and no better than Giselle Harding. I couldn't bear that.'

'It doesn't matter what people say. It's how you live your life that counts.'

'It's all right for you.' Louisa sniffed and pulled herself together. 'I don't want to live in a guesthouse for the rest of my life, and I'm not having people look down on me. I'm going to marry Tobias. Don't you see? I have to. I just have to.'

'Louisa...' Rachel looked at her sister's shut-in face, mouth set in a determined line. 'Very well. I promise I'll respect your wishes and I'll not try to stop you. I won't even say a word against Tobias again. But just promise me one thing.'

'Maybe.' Louisa had such an air of defeat that Rachel's heart went out to her. In the distance, she could hear the familiar sound of Tobias's Bentley racing up the driveway with scant regard for the potholes or any cyclists who might be returning after their day's outing.

If only Peter had survived. It was an open secret that he had always been his father's favourite son, the golden boy who could do no wrong. Tobias could never step into his shoes, however much he did everything within his power to try. There was a bitterness, a disappointment within him Rachel sensed would only grow, especially if he failed to win his father's approval yet again and was sent away in disgrace. She couldn't let Tobias destroy the harbour, not even for Louisa. But she couldn't abandon her sister, however little she might thank her for saying so now.

'If there is ever anything that makes you uneasy, or you are desperately unhappy, you will find some way to let me know. Forget about your pride and what people might say. Just let me know, and I'll come and fetch you, wherever you are. However far away you might be, I'll find some way of getting you home.'

'You'd ask Giselle Harding, you mean. She's rich and people listen to her and want to do things for her because she's famous and beautiful. I'm not having her feeling sorry for me, not for anything.'

'All right, I promise I wouldn't ask Giselle. At least, not unless there is no other choice to make sure you were safe. And even if I did have to ask her, you would never have to meet her. She would want you to be safe because none of this is your doing, any more than it is hers. It wouldn't be pity that would make her help you, but understanding. You can't blame Giselle for something that happened years before Peter ever came to visit us. I think maybe you both have to find a way to forgive him, as well as each other. After all, it was Peter who betrayed you both.'

'I suppose,' said Louisa. She was silent for a few minutes. Rachel heard the front door open, followed by Tobias throwing orders at poor Alice before his footsteps echoed officiously along the corridor towards them. Finally she nodded. 'Yes. Yes, I promise. I won't need to, but I promise.'

Chapter Twenty-Nine

'There's nothing I could say to change her mind,' said Rachel dejectedly as she escaped to the harbour the following afternoon, taking advantage of their guests being out to avoid the tense atmosphere in Enys Hall.

'At least you did your best,' said Jess gently. 'And she knows she's somewhere to turn, should she ever need to.'

'It still doesn't feel enough. Mama was shocked, of course, that she could have allowed herself be put in such a corner. But she wants the best for her, like I do. I can't help feeling Tobias was quite deliberate about this, turning her head and blackmailing her at the same time, to make sure she couldn't change her mind, even if she wanted to. I suspect he is so set on taking control of the harbour, to prove to his father that he is just as good as Peter, that he's quite prepared to try anything to succeed.'

'It's not your sister's fault,' said Jess gently.

'I know. He's cunning enough to know that Louisa would always be the weak point and the way he could get at us.' She shuddered. 'I don't think this was just the harbour and doing everything he could to prove himself to his father. I get this feeling that having Louisa at his side lets him live some kind of fantasy that he really is Peter, or at least that people will see him in the same light.' She looked up at the lay-by on the road, where its familiar occupant had returned. 'You're right, that does look like Tobias.'

'I can't see who else it would be. He's not trying to hide his presence. I'm sure he wants us all to know he's there.'

'It would be easier if we knew what was happening with the harbour,' said Rachel. 'I daren't ask Louisa, not that Tobias would tell her in any case. I don't want him to know I've been asking. Having come this far, I can't see Tobias giving up that easily. I've a nasty feeling this isn't over yet.'

Jess made her way to Enys Hall early next morning, taking care to follow the path along the cliffs that avoided the roadway. To her relief, there was no sign of the motor car on the cliffs.

She pushed through the little gate into the grounds, hitching up her skirts to run across the open space to the kitchens.

'Well, well, what have we here?'

She'd known he wouldn't let it go, that one day or other, he'd be waiting. Sure enough, Tobias was leaning against the Bentley parked where the path from the harbour crossed the driveway.

'Good morning,' she muttered, hastily turning towards the house.

Tobias stepped in front of her, blocking her way. 'It was you, wasn't it.'

'I'm sorry, sir, I'm late.'

'Just like you to run away.' His voice was tight with anger. 'But it was you. I've seen you, sneaking around, watching, working things to your own advantage. How much did she pay you? Or was it the promise of buying more of those cheap little trinkets of yours?'

Jess ignored this. 'As I said, Mr Howells, I'm late. Cook will be wondering where I am.'

'Then she'll have to go on wondering. You've taken enough advantage of these unfortunate women in Enys Hall with your schemes. You'll soon find you can't get away with it. It's a husband's duty to protect his wife. As soon as I'm married to Louisa, you'll soon find out you can't pull the wool over my eyes. You can tell that Harding woman she won't win that easily.'

'I don't know what you're talking about,' she replied. 'Now please let me pass.'

'She won't win. My brother would never have done such a thing, however in thrall he might be to some actress. He had too much loyalty to the family. Just as I do. She can't possibly win.'

'Then you can't be concerned with the likes of me,' she replied, sidestepping him. A hand closed on her arm.

'One rotten apple. That's all it takes. A woman with ambition but no taste or skill, determined to trick others in any way she can. You don't think your father will have a post for much longer in the harbour when he can't even be trusted to keep undesirable enterprises from setting up, so the place is no longer a working harbour.'

'At least it's working.'

'Not for much longer. Once we've got rid of Giselle and her ridiculous claims, I'll make it my business that Mrs Bellamy agrees to the munitions workshops and turns it into a proper working harbour. I'll use my own fleet of trading vessels if I need to. Not that you'll be here to see it.' The grip on her arm tightened. 'I've got unfinished business with you first, you little tart.'

'Well, I don't.' Jess twisted herself, using every muscle that had once wielded a blacksmith's hammer to wrest herself free, jumping back out of reach.

'Leave her alone.' Jess had never been so relieved to find Rachel racing towards them, a look of white-hot anger on her face that had Tobias backing off under its ferocity.

'Good morning, Rachel,' he replied, as smooth as he could, straightening his jacket. 'Surely even you can't object to my checking if your housemaid is happy with her working conditions. Unless, of course, you have something to hide.'

'I know intimidation when I see it,' she retorted. 'I've had enough of your games, Tobias. We've nothing to hide.'

His lips tightened. Muttering something under his breath that sounded suspiciously like 'bitch', he brushed past Rachel and into the house.

'Thank you.' Jess found herself beginning to shake.

'Thank goodness I spotted you. I heard the Bentley arrive, and when he didn't come into the house I had a feeling he was up to something. I take it he was threatening you. Are you all right?'

'I'll live.' Jess rubbed her arm, already reddening from his grip. 'From what he said, he was in such a temper because Giselle is trying to get the land back after all. At least he's told us that.'

'So that was why they stopped the work.'

'But he's still determined to win.'

Rachel sighed. 'I had a feeling he wasn't giving up that easily. Louisa is already ordering wedding dresses. Maybe I was wrong to have told Giselle. It looks as if I could have made it worse for all of us.'

Louisa was married on a damp winter morning, just after Christmas.

Rachel stood among the guests at the Howellses' extravagant London house, complete with paintings by a non-too-skilled follower of Gainsborough, showing more than one bewigged gentleman looking down his nose at the visitors as if claiming to be some aristocratic Howells ancestor. She had a strong urge to jump through the nearest window and run wildly down the elegant streets.

'Bought cheap, and it shows,' remarked a young man at her elbow, following her gaze.

'I beg your pardon?'

'The paintings. Cheap, masquerading as taste. Like the rest of this place. Vulgar glitz. For all they try to hide it. They are in trade, you know.'

'So I'd heard,' replied Rachel drily.

'Friend of the family?'

'The bride.'

'Oh.' The bride clearly met with even less approval. 'Not from London, then?'

'Not in the least.'

'You heard about the first husband, I suppose? That actress has become famous in these new moving pictures. All the women seem to be wearing that hair thing she's become so famous for; I can't see the point of it myself. You'd have thought—'

Rachel hastily stopped avoiding Aunt Flora, who had been attempting for the last half hour to catch her eye. Muttering the barest of excuses, she obeyed the summons to join her aunt and an elderly gentleman encased in a coat that must have fitted him like a glove in his younger days, but was now bursting at the buttons. Very rich and very available, Aunt Flora's complacent smile informed her. Just so long as she moved fast, before any other desperate young lady, tired of struggling to make ends meet, should get her hands on him first.

'What an original dress,' remarked Aunt Flora, as Rachel appeared in her orbit. 'How very striking. I've never see that fashion in Barringtons.'

'It's from a new emporium, Aunt Flora, one that has only recently opened.'

'Really.'

'The fashions are aimed more at women who are pursuing careers. Practical and stylish.'

'And cheap, I suppose.'

'Inexpensive.' Rachel smiled blandly. 'Miss Fairbairn's range of clothing has already become all the rage. She has the wisdom to concentrate on using only the best suppliers and has an excellent dressmaker. I liked the mixture of the bespoke and the affordable. Her eye for design is incomparable.' Aunt Flora pursed her lips. 'You must have heard of her, Aunt, she's been selling the enamelled hair clasps that have become so fashionable.'

'I hope never to see you or your sister in such a thing,' snapped Aunt Flora. 'It's disgraceful. It should be stopped.'

'Well, I think it's a pity Louisa was forbidden to own one. They've become practically de rigueur for weddings. The young woman who creates them is extraordinarily talented. I'm sure she will go far.'

With that, Rachel shot off to disappear amid the matrons chatting among themselves and the single women standing wistfully at the end of the dance floor. She was already tired of the effort of keeping a polite face, particularly when Tobias was smirking pointedly in her direction every time he caught sight of her.

Enjoy the two weeks' grace while he whisked Louisa off on the briefest of honeymoons was his message. As soon as they returned to Cornwall, he would be there at Enys Hall and the harbour, accompanying Louisa every time she visited. He was going to win, whatever it took, and now they would never be free of him.

*

The day after the wedding, with Louisa and Tobias already on their way to Paris, Rachel escaped a visit accompanying her mother to a somewhat tearful Mrs Howells, and made the short walk from their hotel to Annette's shop. She wore a coat which, like the dress for the wedding, had been ordered from Sara Catchpole's new fashion house; in it she felt no different from the other women making their way to and from work. She found herself invigorated by their energy and sense of purpose.

'You look as if you've been enjoying yourself,' said Annette, as she reached the shop.

'The walk here, not the wedding, which was just as painful as I thought it might be. Apart from my dress.'

'I'm glad it was successful,' said Sara Catchpole, emerging from the back of the shop. 'It suits you, that simpler, more modern style, as well as being more practical. I never did hold much with frills and furbelows. Barringtons might have been a lifesaver, but I'm glad I've been able to start my own line. There are so many new fashions, it's good to be able to make clothes women want to wear and can afford.'

Annette left her assistant in charge and the three made their way to the corner tea rooms.

'I'm sorry Louisa cancelled her order for one of Jess's clasps,' said Rachel as they settled down.

'Don't worry, there was already a waiting list. All that happened was that there was a very happy young gentleman who I'm quite sure won his lady's heart and is already preparing for a life of wedded bliss.'

'Louisa was so set on wearing a clasp.' Rachel sighed. 'I have a feeling she thought Giselle's magic might rub off on her. But Tobias forbade her from owning anything Jess makes, even as a gift. He was atrociously rude. He told Mama it was badly made and designed, and looked cheap, and only a woman who had no care for her reputation would wear such a tawdry piece. He kept on about it, all the time Jess was waiting on us at dinner.'

'Poor Jess,' exclaimed Sara. 'I hope she had more sense than to take it to heart.'

'When she's got so many orders already and demand for her new designs is rising? Hardly. I think she's finally got the confidence to trust her customers. It was vile, though. I've never been so embarrassed in my life. But Jess will soon have enough work to support herself; she's only helping us while Alice and the new girl are being trained up to take her place. I'm afraid Louisa didn't say a word, she didn't even sulk; and Mama was determined not to say anything and to keep the peace. All I can do is make sure Jess never has to serve at table again whenever he is there.'

'I'm glad Jess is doing well,' said Sara. 'I miss her, and her hard work. But I can see that she was right to fight for spending her life doing the work she loves. And I can't imagine her living anywhere else but the harbour.'

'No,' agreed Rachel quietly. 'Neither can I.'

Chapter Thirty

The weeks that Tobias and Louisa were away on honey-moon were quiet in the little harbour. Despite it being out of season, Enys Hall was filled with guests eager to catch the drama of the winter light and the wildness of the storms racing in from the sea, leaving Jess to snatch as much time as she could to fulfil her orders.

It felt strange working without Ben at the next bench. Busy as she was fulfilling the commissions from Annette, she missed his presence. At the same time, his brief letters in his slightly crooked handwriting showed his pleasure at finally returning to his old position of teacher.

'Aye well, I knew that'd make him happy,' sighed Mrs Wilkes wistfully, as she read out his descriptions of the rooms he was sharing with a fellow teacher and the evening classes and lectures he had found at the lending library.

'Sounds like he's already making a life for himself again,' said Diana, when she came to the harbour to view the fishing loft on the quayside that had just been repaired and which Jess could see would make an ideal workshop for the two of them to set up their business together. The rent was far more reasonable, and the space a good deal more generous, than any they had viewed in St Ives. And while the size suited their needs perfectly, the loft's position gave it the peace and quiet they both craved, accompanied by the gentle bustle of the little harbour, with its thriving shops and cafés.

'So he is,' said Jess. She didn't like to say that for all his obvious enjoyment of being able to teach once more, there was a slightly wistful air to his letters, as if his heart was still in the harbour. It would pass, she told herself.

Besides, Ben was well out of the harbour now the honeymoon was over and Tobias and Louisa were back settled in the house in St Ives. Despite no more signs of work on the cleared piece of land, Tobias was making it abundantly clear that he had no intention of relinquishing his hold over them all. Most mornings as Jess made her way up to the Hall, and every evening as she made her way home, the Bentley was in its place in the lay-by.

Within days of the happy couple's return, Tobias had been seen walking through the harbour, making his presence felt in each business before standing pointedly on the quay, looking over to the empty land on the far side that was still awaiting its fate.

'You are right, this would be perfect,' agreed Diana, as they stepped into the long attic room, made light and airy by windows looking over the sea. 'There's plenty of space for me to do my silverwork and you to work on your enamelling.'

'If only we knew what was happening with the harbour,' said Jess.

Between them, they could make this work, she was sure of it. Diana was also getting more orders for her silverwork after the samples Annette had placed in her shop. They were getting to the point where they could begin to train up some of the young women from the harbour to join them in their little enterprise.

With Morwenna already needing more seamstresses and embroiderers for her expanding business, there was beginning to be a chatter of young women in the winding streets and on the quay. Jess loved hearing their flirtatious banter with fishermen mending their boats, echoing among the call of seagulls each evening; the sound of life returning to the harbour.

Between the little businesses and the visitors, a quiet air of prosperity had begun to appear. Some of the abandoned cottages in the cove already had new families, with overgrown gardens being cleared to plant vegetables and the sound of children playing in the evening light, while smoke rose up from the chimneys, with the warm glow of lamps flickering inside as darkness fell.

Jess sighed. She was tired of fighting. All she wanted to do was to concentrate on her enamel work and make her designs the best they could be. She still had more orders than she could easily fulfil, and with several well-known movie stars having recently ordered a version of the clasp with the sailing boat against a Cornish sunset, she was beginning to be confident she would soon have even more.

As they left, she took a last look at the room, with its peaceful warmth, sunlight spilling through its emptiness, waiting for them to fill it with workbenches and the tap of hammer on metal. It was all she had ever dreamed of, to be able to stay in the harbour and make her living there.

Jess' stomach lurched. The trouble was, she acknowledged, she and Diana would only have one chance at setting up their business. For all they had both scrimped and saved, neither of them had enough set by to start again, should this one fail, or Tobias be determined to pay her back by driving them out by any means necessary. She was going to have to explain things to Diana; she couldn't ask her to take that risk. Besides, if she was going to be able to fulfil all her orders and create new designs, she couldn't waste any more time and energy on fighting Tobias. It seemed she might, after all, end up having to move away.

'It would make more sense for you to set up somewhere else,' said Rachel, as she and Jess finished their work at Enys Hall and took their cups of tea out into the fragile sunshine, with its first promise of the approaching spring, to sit on a garden bench overlooking the harbour. 'Tobias is already badgering Mama whenever he and Louisa visit. He says he's looking out for Louisa's interests, and their son's.'

Jess raised her eyebrows. 'So already it's a son they're having.'

'Naturally. Tobias expects nothing else.' Rachel absently crumbled her slice of Madeira cake into a thousand pieces, lost in thought. 'Ben could still secure you work at the Birmingham School of Jewellery. That would give you more security while you build up your business.' She grimaced. 'I'm sure anything would be better than scrubbing floors and mending curtains here.'

'Funnily enough, I've a feeling I'll miss it,' said Jess, with a smile. They were silent for a few minutes. 'It doesn't have to be Birmingham,' she said at last. 'Thanks to you, Aunt Sara seems to have finally accepted that my heart will never be in dressmaking. After you visited her when you were there for Louisa's wedding, she's been twisting as many arms as she could find to secure me a space in London, one big enough for Diana too, if she wishes.'

'London?' Rachel looked at her in dismay.

'It would make sense. Our main outlets are there, so we wouldn't have to rely on transporting them such a distance. Diana has her family, and her father may one day come round to seeing her work as respectable. Besides, Aunt Sara has always wanted me and her to rent a house together so we could look after Dad.'

'But the harbour needs him as harbourmaster more than ever.'

'He might not want to join us right now, but one day he will be too old to be out in all weathers. He'll want to retire in peace some day.'

'That's true.' Rachel went back to crumbling cake, despite having been ravenous after a day of cleaning and changing beds. 'Jess, are you sure?'

'I need to consider it. I have to be realistic, I may not have any choice. Aunt Sara is coming to visit us next week. She said we could discuss it then.'

'But if you went to London...' Rachel's voice drifted into silence.

'I wouldn't be close to Ben?'

'Yes.' Rachel straightened her shoulders determinedly. 'I didn't expect you to stay here once he had gone, Jess. Especially after Tobias tried to threaten you. I know you needed to take the chance of getting your business on its feet, but it always made sense for you to join him teaching. I understand how close you are to him.'

'You're a fine one to talk.'

'Me?' Rachel stared at her.

'You really think that if Ben marries me, he'll be happy?'

'Of course. That's all I want, with all my heart. For you both to be happy.'

'Well, you've a funny way of showing it.'

'I beg your pardon?'

Jess grinned as Rachel's chin went up. 'It's no good talking to me as if you were a fine lady speaking to her maid, you know.'

'I'm not!'

'I hope not, because I want us to always be friends. You and Ben. Don't you see? I'm very fond of Ben, I always have been for as long as I can remember. But he would never be happy with me as a wife. And, more to the point, I'd never be happy with him.' She coloured slightly. 'And no, not just because I know he'll love you until the day he dies. I owe him more than I can ever say as my teacher. But that's not the same as passion. I don't want to be a pupil all my life. Yes, I know Ben would never treat me like that,' she added, as Rachel began to protest. 'But it would always be there.'

She took Rachel's hands in hers and squeezed them hard. 'Don't you see? Even if I did love him, it would never work. Ben is a wonderful teacher, the best I could ever have wished for. But he's also a proud craftsman. I'm not sure he would ever have found it easy to see a pupil overtake him while he struggles with his injuries. I may have spurred him on to get back to working the best he can, but he always hated that I could do the things he could once do with ease and may never be able to do again. Don't you see, that would eat away at him, day by day, until he could bear it no longer? He is proud of me, but I am also a torment. It seems to me that would never be the good basis for a marriage.'

'But you could find a way.'

'Only if I was in love with him. Or if he loved me with all his heart and soul. He could never be happy with me, loving someone else.'

Rachel shook her head. 'It's impossible.'

'Because of your family?'

'Ben would hate it at Enys Hall. Mama's friends would laugh at him behind his back.'

'But that's just here. If you went to Birmingham, you wouldn't be the lady of the manor, any more than Ben would be the son of a blacksmith. In a place where no one knew you, who would care?'

'I can't leave my mother to struggle here on her own.'

'Yes, you can. And anyhow, she wouldn't struggle. Not after all your hard work. The guesthouse is earning enough for her to be able to employ people to help her. She wants you to be happy. I don't think you'll ever be happy until you find work for which you have a passion, body and soul. I saw the way you were so at home in London. A city like Birmingham would give you plenty of scope to battle the world.'

'You don't understand. How can Ben ever forgive me? It was because of me he was so horribly injured. I ruined his life. It's my fault he can't do the work he loves. How could we live with that between us?'

'Ben could have died or been wounded at any moment in France, just as you could have done. You were both incredibly brave and knew what you were risking.'

Rachel sighed. 'The trouble is, I don't know how he feels any more. He's always avoided me. I'm sure I was part of the reason he left as soon as he could.'

'I'm sure that's because he loves you too much to cause you pain. He's just as proud as you are. And he knows how impossible it would be here to overcome the distance between you. I've seen the way he looks at you, Rachel. He left because he loves you, and he wants you to be free to be happy. I'm sure neither of you will ever find happiness if you are apart.'

Chapter Thirty-One

Aunt Sara arrived a few days later.

'I hope you don't mind,' she said as she hugged Jess. 'I've brought a friend to see you.'

'Yes, of course.' Jess stepped back to allow the woman encased in a veil to step inside the cottage.

'Don't worry, Jess. I'm not expecting you to find me a bed for the night – my assistant is booking us a hotel in St Ives.'

'Giselle!'

Giselle had pushed back her veil. 'It's good to see you again, Jess.'

Jess frowned at her anxiously. 'Did you know Tobias is here in the harbour most days?'

'Yes. Don't worry, I've every intention of keeping out of his way. It's his father I have business with. He's finally agreed to meet me in St Ives. I certainly have no wish to see Tobias again. I can't go up to Enys Hall; it wouldn't be exactly tactful. But perhaps you and Rachel would like to join me at the hotel this evening? I'll send the motor car. My chauffeur is completely trustworthy and not even Tobias would attempt to intimidate him.'

'I would love to and I'm sure Rachel will too. I'll tell her when I go up there tomorrow morning.'

'Thank you. Perhaps we could walk down to the harbour? I would like to see it.'

'With pleasure. I can show you how it's changed, Aunt Sara. There are tea rooms on the quay.'

'That sounds perfect,' said Giselle.

With the milling of early visitors in the harbour, no one looked twice at the two elegantly dressed women, clearly from the city. One or two recognised Aunt Sara, but took little notice of her friend. Giselle had a way of not looking in the least like the film star, or even particularly beautiful. Certainly not striking. Jess couldn't help smiling to herself as they took a seat in a corner overlooking the harbour, Giselle half turned away, with Aunt Sara and Jess providing a screen between her and the rest of the diners.

'Is that Peter's land over there?' asked Giselle, once the waitress had brought their order of tea and cake.

'Yes,' said Jess. 'You can see where it's been cleared.'

'To build a factory.'

'Yes.'

'I can see how it would ruin the harbour for the visitors.'

'And without the visitors, most of the businesses would not be here.'

'Which would hardly encourage the others to stay,' added Aunt Sara.

'Yes, I can see that.' Giselle sipped her tea, deep in thought. 'It's beautiful here. I can see why Peter loved it so much and why he wished to keep it like this and not let it go.'

'You can't live in the past,' said Aunt Sara gently.

'That was my thought too. But I can see this has managed to keep the past and the present in harmony. You are right, Jess. It has a future, one that I can see can serve both the people who live here and the visitors. I'd hate to see this destroyed.'

Aunt Sara was frowning at her. 'Are you sure about this, Giselle?'

'Never more so. I wasn't certain when I came over from America, or even when we arrived just now. But now I am. I know exactly what I need to do.'

Jess looked up quickly at the sound of a motor car coming to rest just outside the harbour. To her relief, it was a gleaming Rolls-Royce Silver Ghost, not a black Bentley.

'The chauffeur is for me,' said Giselle regretfully. 'I had better go. I have an appointment with Mr Howells in St Ives and I have no intention of being late. Let's hope he finally sees sense.'

The rest of the day passed in an agony of suspense. At every footstep, every roar of an engine on the road above, Jess expected to be confronted by a furious Tobias, ready to blame her for dragging Giselle to see the harbour and make trouble for him. But there was nothing. Everything was quiet the following day too, as Jess left Dad to proudly show Aunt Sara the improvements to the harbour, while she made her way to Enys Hall.

That evening, Giselle's chauffeur arrived to convey the three of them to the hotel on the cliffs just outside St Ives, where Giselle was waiting.

'Well?' demanded Aunt Sara, as they were shown into the suite of rooms overlooking the sea. 'Did he agree?'

'In the end.'

Jess blinked. 'Mr Howells handed over the land?'

'Not exactly. We came to an agreement. I gave him the market price. Well, rather more than the market price. I gave him what he demanded.'

'You bought the land?' Rachel stared at Giselle in astonishment. 'But I thought it was already yours.'

'It was worth it. This way the Howellses get to save face and I can keep the harbour safe. It seems a fair exchange to me.'

'But surely he didn't give in that easily?' said Jess.

'He might not have done if Tobias had managed to get you all to kowtow to his bullying,' said Giselle. 'Rather, his father had started to think it was making the Howellses look foolish and ineffectual, and the harbour was more trouble than it was worth. And that was also thanks to the success of turning Enys Hall into a guesthouse and enabling the businesses in the harbour to thrive.'

'I still can't believe he gave in that easily,' said Rachel.

'Well, I did have my lawyer with me,' replied Giselle dryly. 'The best money can buy, and Mr Howells knew it. He soon saw it was the only way to avoid a lawsuit: one that I most likely would have won, which would have been highly embarrassing for the family reputation. Not to mention their name dragged through the papers for nothing. It would all have been vile, of course, and everything about me and Peter would have come out. I'm sorry, Rachel, I didn't want to hurt your sister any more than she has been already, but I was prepared to see my own name dragged through the mud. I'm not sure Mr Howells was prepared to take that risk for himself, not even for the convenience and status of owning a private harbour. I'm sure he'll find somewhere else that will not prove quite so troublesome.'

'So Tobias will have no choice but to go to South America,' sighed Rachel, as the four of them sat down to dinner in Giselle's private suite. 'I still wish I could have changed my sister's mind. There must have been something more I could have done.'

'You did your best, Rachel,' said Sara. 'There really is nothing more you can do. She's not going to listen now.'

'I'll certainly help if she ever needs it,' added Giselle. 'I doubt Tobias will change; his sort never do. I saw how he could be when he came to threaten me after Peter was killed, and the way he and his father tried to blacken my name and prevent me from ever working again when it suited them. They were quite prepared to let me starve in a gutter, or sink to having to sell myself to survive. They clearly saw it as no concern of theirs.'

'Just as they didn't care what happened to anyone in the harbour, so long as they could get their way,' said Rachel. 'I'd do anything to keep Louisa from harm.'

'You still might be able to, one day,' said Giselle gently.

Rachel nodded. 'I hope so. At least it has made me realise what I want to do with my life. You were right, Jess, Mama can employ people to help her now. And if the harbour continues to thrive, she could easily employ a manager, or even sell Enys Hall to someone younger who wants to take on running a guesthouse, and live in one of the smaller cottages instead. I feel I've been a little mad since the war, but my mind is perfectly clear now. I know exactly what I want to do. I learnt so much when I was out in France during the war, and it has haunted me ever since that I could do so little for the women and children. But at least now I can use those skills to help women and children here who are suffering to escape to better lives.'

'I'm glad you've found a way,' said Jess, returning her smile.

Rachel turned to Giselle. 'So, now it's yours, what will you do with the land?'

'I'm not sure. To be honest, I wasn't sure I wanted to ever come here again after this. I didn't want to spend any time in the places Peter had loved and I certainly didn't want to find myself running into Louisa or any of the Howells.'

'But now they won't be here any more,' said Jess. 'Not now their summer house in St Ives is definitely for sale.'

'Yes, that had occurred to me. And, to be truthful, I feel

at home here. Don't hate me, Rachel, but it feels as if this is where the best of Peter remains. The part I loved and once thought would never leave me. The short time I've been here, I've felt that, for all his faults, that part of him will never leave here. I'm considering purchasing one of the empty cottages behind the harbour. I need a place to retreat, where I'm not known and can walk down the street without the need to be dressed as the glamorous movie star. Where I can dig in my garden and simply be the anonymous woman in the local tea rooms, watching the world go by.'

'That sounds an excellent idea,' said Aunt Sara. 'And if you start your own movie company, you could even use the land to create a studio, or for the making of costumes and props.'

'That had crossed my mind,' said Giselle. 'I rather like the idea of being based here, away from the madness of the cities and the big studios.'

'There are plenty of talented people here, and with the railways it's possible to move anything,' put in Jess.

Giselle laughed. 'Tobias should have known from the start that, faced with such determined women, he could never win. Although he's the kind of man who'll never admit as much, until the day he dies, and persist in viewing us as weak and silly and quite unable to run our own lives.'

'More fool him,' sniffed Rachel scornfully.

'Quite.' Giselle turned her gaze out through the window, where the evening sun was sinking over Porthmeor Beach, catching the sails of fishing boats and pleasure yachts making their way across St Ives Bay. 'For now, my life will be in America or London. But that will not be for ever. I'd like to know I have a place to come back to. Somewhere that will always be home.'

'I can't think of anywhere better,' said Jess, with a smile.

Chapter Thirty-Two

Rachel knocked tentatively on the door of the teaching room in the Birmingham School of Jewellery.

'Come in!'

She took a deep breath and pushed her way inside.

'Miss Bellamy!' Ben hastily put down his work and jumped to his feet.

'I was passing,' said Rachel, trying to ignore the look of dismay mingled with surprise on his face. 'I couldn't come all this way and not visit.'

'I've a class starting in a few minutes,' he muttered awkwardly.

'So they told me; I promised not to detain you for long.' She fished out the tin from the bag slung over her shoulder. 'I told them I was bringing this from your mother.'

'Oh.' He coloured slightly. 'I have explained to her I can cook perfectly well for myself and there are cafés all around my lodgings, but she does insist on sending me provisions.'

'This one is fruitcake. She made another for me. I'm sure she thought I was about to starve too. Although I'm not sure my Aunt Julia would allow me to go quite that far. Even she has to admit I need some kind of sustenance to wait on her hand and foot.'

He turned away, back to his bench. 'So you are visiting Birmingham.'

'To be truthful, my aunt is under the impression it's a permanent arrangement.'

'And is it?'

'Maybe. It depends.' He swung round, frowning at her. 'Oh, not on you, Mr Wilkes.'

'I didn't think it would, Miss Bellamy,' he retorted.

'Good. So you can put that male vanity of yours to one side.'

This time he scowled. 'Did you really come all this way just to insult me?'

'Not entirely. I thought you might like to know I've found paid employment with a charity working with women and children in need of refuge. It seems my experience in France might have its uses after all.'

'So it should.'

'It's what I want to do, Ben. I don't want to be rich; I want to feel I'm doing something worthwhile with my life. And I'm afraid I'm going to be able to disappoint Aunt Julia before long and assert my independence.'

'I'm glad,' he said, not meeting her eyes.

'The obvious choice was London, of course. But then Jess suggested I might want to try Birmingham.'

'She did?'

'Yes. She made me see that if I came here, it would be like starting again, like it was in France. No one knows me here. I'm just another woman.'

'Clearly an educated one,' he replied dryly.

'But that doesn't matter so much any more; so much changed during the war, it can't go back to the way it was.'

He was silent. There was a stubborn, shut expression on his face she knew all too well. Despair went through her. Maybe Jess had been mistaken.

'I don't want to make things awkward for you, Ben. After

everything that happened, I'll understand if you don't want to ever speak to me again. But I am determined to take up the post. Don't you see, Ben, this is the only way I can stop their faces, the ones we couldn't save. Oh, I know I can't save everyone, but at least I'm going to try.'

'I wouldn't expect you to do anything else,' he replied. 'I know you far too well.'

'I'm so sorry, Ben. I'll never forgive myself for taking out the ambulance that day, for what happened to you. I don't expect you to ever forgive me either.'

'There's nothing to forgive.' He reached out and brushed the tears from her cheeks with his good hand. 'None of us escaped unscathed from the battlegrounds out there in France, any more than those who struggled on at home. But we are making our lives again with what we have and building something new.' He kissed her gently. 'And I will forever be grateful for my life, whatever it brings.'

Rachel's arms crept around him, holding him tight. 'I lost you once, Ben. However hard I've tried, I can't stop loving you. I love you more than ever. I don't ever want to lose you again.'

'I feel I should warn you: I'm not an easy person to live with these days.'

'And you think I am?'

He laughed at that. 'I'm certain you're not. That's exactly what I fell in love with in the first place. The headstrong, irascible woman who speaks her mind. The woman I'll love, body and soul, until the day I die. I'll always love you, dearest Rachel, with all my heart. But, even in France, we both knew it was impossible. I don't want to be the cause of any hurt or any rift between you and your family.'

Rachel returned his kiss. 'So much of the world has changed since then. I'm sure if my father and brothers were still alive, they'd consider it their duty to chase you off, in some old-fashioned idea that they were protecting me from myself. But my mother has enough to worry about with poor Louisa. She wants me to be happy, not marry for money or security. I think she finally understands I could only ever marry for love – deep, passionate love. Although I'm rather afraid Aunt Julia will never be satisfied with less than an earl.' She kissed him again. 'But that is largely due to preferring to have a personal attendant for the rest of her days.'

His arms tightened. 'Darling Rachel, you are worth so much more than that.'

'I quite agree,' said Rachel. 'And besides, who else would put up with a wife who will work night and day to save all those in her care?' Her eyes filled with tears. 'Or understand the terrors of her dreams?'

'We always worked well together when every moment could be our last.' He drew her closer. 'I have a feeling that the rest is something we will always be able to work out between us.'

Summer had come once more to the little harbour. The morning's rain had cleared, leaving a calm and sunny afternoon. Already painters were settling down at the best vantage points and the walking party staying at Enys Hall had set out across the cliffs to make the most of the rest of the day. A boat was arriving, bringing visitors from St Ives and to take weary explorers back to their hotels.

Even Mrs Wilkes had been lured out to take a cup of tea at the tearooms on the quay, where the outside tables were being brought out from under cover as the sky cleared.

'You'm as busy as ever, I see,' she remarked, as Jess emerged from the old fishing loft on the quay, stretching out her shoulders. 'It's good to see the place a hive of activity again.'

'Jess and Diana have done wonders,' said Morwenna, joining her mother for a slice of the tearoom's fabled fruit loaf. 'You'd never think that old loft had been used for anything else.'

'We were so lucky to secure it before one of the painters from St Ives spotted its potential,' replied Jess.

She looked over to where she could see Dad standing on the quayside, exchanging views on the state of the sea with the fishermen, as a boat laden with yet more visitors made its way into the harbour. Walkers were making their way down from the cliffs towards the welcome refreshment of the tearooms, while a photographer was setting up her camera on the cliffs, ready to capture the play of sunlight on the incoming rollers.

Jess sat down on a nearby bench and took the letter from Rachel out of her pocket, reading it again with a smile. Her new post sounded terrifying, but Rachel was clearly having the time of her life, especially now she and Ben had found a small house to rent, so she could finally escape her aunt's attempts to make her change her mind about so imprudent a match, even for a woman who had so few other options in life.

Jess glanced up at Enys Hall. There had been no word of Mrs Bellamy's views on her daughter's most unsuitable engagement. But, so the whisper had gone round the harbour once the news leaked out, it was far better than poor Miss Rachel remaining a spinster, and at least young Wilkes was a respectable craftsman rather than some married man or rake who could turn an unmarried woman's head and lead her to all kinds of disaster and break her poor mother's heart, and that would never do. Besides, didn't Mrs Bellamy have quite enough to worry about with her youngest child settled so far away, and her not knowing when she might get to see her new baby granddaughter?

As she returned to her letter, Jess's eye was caught by a group of painters on the quay, intent on capturing the scene in front of them. There was something about the bend of the head of the girl nearest to her, the intensity of her concentration… But it couldn't be. Jess sighed. It had to be a trick of the light. The power of wishful thinking.

A shadow fell on the page. 'She insisted on coming today, you see.'

Jess jumped to her feet, not daring to trust her eyes. 'Frank!'

'Hello Jess.' He was browned, hair bleached by strong sun, but his smile held the same warmth.

'I was so sure you had stayed in France! Did you find your village?'

'It was good to see it has been rebuilt, and that some people I remembered had returned.'

'I see.' A hollow opened up in her heart. 'So you will go back.'

'They wanted us to stay. There are not many young people there, most have gone to the cities to find work, or just not come back. Our old house is there; it's a ruin, but it could be rebuilt.'

'Oh.'

'But it is no longer home. Charlotte missed her life here. I'd forgotten she was little more than a baby when we left, too young to remember much of our life before the soldiers came. This is the only home she has ever really known.'

'But not you.'

He sighed. 'You can't go back, Jess. However much you try, however much you long for it with all your heart, you can't go back to the past. There were good memories, ones I was glad to find again. But it's not my home. However hard I tried, I couldn't feel a part of the life there. If my parents had been alive, it might have been different. I would have had ties to them, obligations to make sure they were looked after as they grew older. Perhaps then it would have been harder. Or if Charlotte had felt at home there. But we were both outsiders.'

'I'm sorry.'

'I'm glad I went. It answered a question that was always in my mind. It made me see it's not just a place that is important, but the people who surround you. This is my life, here in Cornwall. It's the only life I want.' His face was wistful. 'Since I've been back, I've heard of many changes.'

'Did you hear that Diana and I have set up a workshop together here?'

His eyes rested on her face. 'And that Ben was soon to be married.'

'I so wish I'd realised how he felt about Rachel.'

'I'm sorry,' he said gently. 'Time is a healer, I think we have all found.'

Jess stared at him. A vision shot into her mind of him standing at the workshop door as she and Ben pored over her designs and the way he would not meet her gaze. Her heart began to hammer in her chest.

'What I meant was that I hate the thought of two people who loved each other being kept apart. I should have known that what was breaking Ben's heart was more than the injury to his hand. If I'd realised, I'd have knocked their heads together ages ago.'

'But I thought...' She saw him swallow. 'Everyone assumed.'

'That Ben had no other choice, and I'd look after him for the rest of my life?' She took his hand. 'Of course I would

322

have looked after Ben. I love him too much not to, just as I love Dad and Aunt Sara and everyone who's been my family all my life. And I value his advice on my work; he was always the best of teachers when it came to the practicalities of metalwork. But that doesn't make it a meeting of soul mates, or the kind of love I'd want in a husband. With my work I don't ever settle for second best; it's not in my nature, it never will be. And I would rather live alone than not be with someone I could love with my heart and soul.'

'Heart and soul. I think it took me to travel so far away, to find that too.'

'Then you are planning to stay?'

'Always,' he replied, with a smile that twisted her insides into a knot. 'Everything I love is here.'

There was so much she wanted to ask, so much she wanted to say. But already the smallest of the painters had thrown down her sketchbook and was running towards them. Charlotte had grown, seeming to have turned, over so short a time, from a child to a young woman. As she reached them, she was smiling with delight. She flung her arms around Jess, hugging her tight.

'It's good to see you again,' said Jess, kissing the upturned face that was almost as brown as her brother's and had lengthened towards the woman she would be.

'Jess-i-ca,' she said, rolling the word around in her mouth as if to savour every syllable.

Jess heard Frank's sharp intake of breath. She found his hand. The pressure of her grasp was returned so tightly she almost cried out. Then it eased.

'I missed you, Charlotte,' she said, as if nothing out of the ordinary had taken place. 'I'm glad you are back.'

Charlotte smiled hesitantly, as if suddenly self-conscious. 'Yes,' she whispered, nodding in her old expressive way, as she made her way back to her easel, soon back to being engrossed in capturing the harbour and the distant roll of the sea.

'I didn't think, I couldn't believe, she ever would,' said Frank, voice cracking. 'She spoke a little when we were in France, but she hasn't said a word since we have been back here.'

'But she has now. This is the beginning you've been working for ever since you arrived here with nothing more than your lives, the night of the shipwreck.'

'Maybe.'

'I'm sure it will take time,' said Jess gently, seeing the fear back in his eyes. 'But at least now there's hope that she will one day find her voice again.'

'I hope.'

'I'm certain.' She grasped his hand, pulling him away from the harbour, up the cliff path towards Enys Hall, where Cook was setting out afternoon tea in the garden, ready for the guests returning from their expedition.

Partway up, breathless from the speed of their escape, they sank into a hollow of grass, out of sight of Mrs Bellamy's guests and secluded from the business of the harbour below.

'Perhaps it was good to go back, after all,' said Frank. She could see the tears in his eyes, the raw grief still clearly evident. Despite the rounding of his features, she could still make out the boy who had run from unimaginable horrors only to watch so many of his fellow refugees drown. The one pulled from the raging sea at the last moment of his life, who had refused to leave his little sister, his every last breath focused on keeping her safe. The one she would love until the day she died.

'Charlotte will find her own way,' said Jess. 'You've given her the strength to make her own life.'

'Yes.' His brows creased into a tight knot. 'I should be glad she is beginning to speak at last. But instead I feel empty.'

'Perhaps because your purpose has gone and it's time for you to make your own life?'

'It feels I need to make the world again, and I'm not sure how.'

Jess held him close. 'I'm not sure anyone does,' she said. 'Not after so much suffering and loss. Yet we can both see the world being rebuilt around us, every day.'

'Yes, that is true.' His arms went around her, holding her tight. 'And now I know that I have found my true home.' He kissed her. 'I heard from Diana that your metalwork is beautiful and so very in demand. I can't wait to see what you have done.'

'In a while,' smiled Jess, curling up against him in the warmth of the sun. Around them, the grass hummed with insects. On the hillside above, fat bumblebees, laden with pollen, made their slow way from flower to flower.

Jess breathed in deep the scent of sun-warmed grass. A tug of sea breeze on her face brought the distant call of gulls and the crash of rollers against the cliffs.

Below in the little harbour, fishing boats rattled at anchor, mingled with the voices of those leaving the boat bringing the next party of visitors to join the busyness of the quay. Patterns were forming in her head, ready to be sketched out this evening and tried in the workshop the next day.

'Come on,' she said, pulling Frank to his feet as several walkers began to make their way up towards their hiding place, en route to Enys Hall. 'It looks as if Charlotte and her party are finishing for the day. I can't wait to show you both my workshop, and I'm sure Charlotte will love tea and cake at the tea rooms before you have to go back to St Ives.'

'I have a motorised van now, so it is only a few minutes.

And maybe, we will find a place here. I feel I would like this to be my home.'

'I feel certain it will,' said Jess, returning his kiss. Tucking her arm through his, they made their way back down towards the bustle of the harbour, to where Charlotte was waiting.

Acknowledgements

First of all, I would like to thank everyone at Orion, who have all been so great to work with during such a difficult time, especially my editors Victoria Oundjian and Charlotte Mursell, as well as Olivia Barber, Amber Bates and Clare Wallis. Thanks also to my wonderful agent, Judith Murdoch, for the endless support and encouragement, not to mention the inspirational bouncing around of ideas.

A special thankyou to fellow authors, including Carol Lovekin for the (virtual) writerly chats, combined with the occasional therapeutic rant, along with the Wyrd Sisters, Trisha Ashley and Louise Marley, and the NW Novelistas. One day there will be cake again!

I couldn't have done this without the support of friends and family, as well as the best of neighbours, Dave and Nerys, Delyth and Catrin and their help with the menagerie.

Last, but by no means least, a four-legged thanks to Miss Phoebe the collie cross who, even in the midst of a global pandemic, continues to focus the mind on the important things in life, primarily long walks, good company, and biscuits…

Credits

Juliet Greenwood and Orion Fiction would like to thank everyone at Orion who worked on the publication of *The Girl with the Silver Clasp* in the UK.

Editorial
Charlotte Mursell
Olivia Barber

Copy editor
Clare Wallis

Proof reader
John Garth

Audio
Paul Stark
Amber Bates

Contracts
Anne Goddard
Paul Bulos
Jake Alderson

Design
Debbie Holmes
Rachael Lancaster

Joanna Ridley
Nick May

Editorial Management
Charlie Panayiotou
Jane Hughes
Alice Davis

Finance
Jasdip Nandra
Afeera Ahmed
Elizabeth Beaumont
Sue Baker

Production
Ruth Sharvell

Marketing
Tanjiah Islam

Publicity
Patricia Deveer

Sales

Jen Wilson
Esther Waters
Victoria Laws
Rachael Hum
Ellie Kyrke-Smith
Frances Doyle

Georgina Cutler

Operations

Jo Jacobs
Sharon Willis
Lisa Pryde
Lucy Brem

'I absolutely loved it. Hester is one heck of a woman!'
HEIDI SWAIN, *Sunday Times* bestselling author of
A Taste of Home

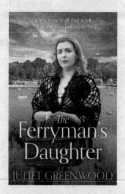

Can Hester help her family escape desperate poverty and fulfil her dreams?

Cornwall, 1908. Hester's life has never been easy. Her father is a hard man to like, spending more time, and money, in the local than with his family. After her beloved mother dies and an injury forces her father to give up his job as the ferryman, Hester must care for her young brother and sister and keep the family afloat.

As the years pass, Hester must row the ferry night and day to keep them all from starvation, while her hopes of working in a kitchen and becoming a cook slip further and further away.

But just how far is Hester willing to go to make her dream a reality? And as the threat of war comes ever closer to the Cornish coast, will it bring opportunities or despair for Hester and her family?

Escape to the Cornish coast for a gripping saga of family, courage and hope